Correct!
Prevent!
Improve!

Driving Improvement through Problem Solving and Corrective and Preventive Action

Also available from ASQ Quality Press:

After the Quality Audit: Closing the Loop on the Audit Process,
Second Edition
J. P. Russell and Terry Regel

Process Auditing Techniques Guide
J. P. Russell

How to Audit the Process-Based QMS
Dennis R. Arter, Charles A. Cianfrani, and John E. (Jack) West

The Internal Auditing Pocket Guide
J. P. Russell

Quality Audits for Improved Performance, Third Edition
Dennis R. Arter

Internal Quality Auditing
Denis Pronovost

Quality Audit Handbook, Second Edition
ASQ Quality Audit Division

To request a complimentary catalog of ASQ Quality Press publications,
call 800-248-1946, or visit our Web site at http://qualitypress.asq.org .

Correct!
Prevent!
Improve!

Driving Improvement through Problem Solving and Corrective and Preventive Action

Jeanne Ketola
Kathy Roberts

ASQ Quality Press
Milwaukee, Wisconsin

American Society for Quality, Quality Press, Milwaukee 53203
© 2003 by ASQ
All rights reserved. Published 2003
Printed in the United States of America

12 11 10 09   5 4 3

Library of Congress Cataloging-in-Publication Data

Ketola, Jeanne.
   Correct!, prevent!, improve! : driving improvement through problem
solving and corrective and preventive action / Jeanne Ketola, Kathy
Roberts.
      p. cm.
   Includes bibliographical references and index.
   ISBN 0-87389-575-4 (Soft Cover : alk. paper)
   1. Management. 2. Problem solving. 3. Decision making. 4. Teams in
the workplace. 5. Organizational effectiveness. I. Roberts, Kathy. II.
Title.

HD31.K4616 2003
658.4'03—dc21   2003004237

ISBN 0-87389-575-4

Publisher: William A. Tony
Acquisitions Editor: Annemieke Koudstaal
Project Editor: Paul O'Mara
Production Administrator: Randall Benson
Special Marketing Representative: Robin Barry

ASQ Mission: The American Society for Quality advances individual,
organizational, and community excellence worldwide through learning,
quality improvement, and knowledge exchange.

Attention Bookstores, Wholesalers, Schools, and Corporations: ASQ Quality
Press books, videotapes, audiotapes, and software are available at quantity
discounts with bulk purchases for business, educational, or instructional use.
For information, please contact ASQ Quality Press at 800-248-1946, or write to
ASQ Quality Press, P.O. Box 3005, Milwaukee, WI 53201-3005.

To place orders or to request a free copy of the ASQ Quality Press Publications
Catalog, including ASQ membership information, call 800-248-1946. Visit our
Web site at www.asq.org or http://qualitypress.asq.org.

   Printed on acid-free paper

Quality Press
600 N. Plankinton Avenue
Milwaukee, Wisconsin 53203
Call toll free 800-248-1946
Fax 414-272-1734
www.asq.org
http://www.asq.org/quality-press
http://standardsgroup.asq.org
E-mail: authors@asq.org

To Chuck, Jon, Lida, and Tim for your patience and understanding.
You have improved my life beyond measure;
In memory of my Mom and to my Dad who always provides
an unlimited supply of support and love;
To Wayne and Terry whose humor keeps me going;
To Kathy for being a great colleague and friend.
—Jeanne

To Ryan and Austin for giving me your unconditional love and support;
To Mom and Mark for giving me inspiration and guidance;
To James for showing me how to continually pursue challenges;
To Jeanne for being a wonderful business partner and friend.
—Kathy

Failure is only the opportunity to begin again more intelligently.

Henry Ford

Table of Contents

Introduction

No organization is lucky enough to get through life without problems. In fact, in some organizations, solving problems for good is the exception rather than the rule. So much time and energy is spent on dealing with problems after they occur and trying to correct them. When this happens, little or no time is left to find ways to prevent them from happening in the first place, much less finding the time to drive improvement.

This book was written as a direct result of the confusion and frustration we see our clients experiencing when trying to implement processes for problem solving, corrective and preventive action, and continual improvement. Many organizations simply don't know how to get started. We see time and time again that many lack the very fundamental elements of these basic processes. Because of this, we have written the book in a very straightforward manner with terms that are not new and not intended to be innovative. Instead, the terms are meant to be simple to understand and useful for the problem-solving team.

Although the concepts of corrective action, preventive action, and continual improvement described in this book are based on the ANSI/ISO/ASQ Q9001:2008—Quality Management System Requirements, this book was purposely written to appeal to all organizations regardless of their size, location, or industry. It is intended to give the reader a general understanding of an approach for solving problems and is written in terms that are easy to understand. This book is a concise, step-by-step guide that takes the reader through a basic problem-solving process while describing how the concepts of corrective and preventive action are incorporated.

The tools found in the book are basic tools that problem-solving teams can use to get started. They are not intended to be the only tools used to solve problems. In fact, there are more in-depth problem-solving tools available that require statistical analysis as well as advanced problem-solving skills. The basic tools have been included because, from our experience in facilitating teams and auditing quality management systems, we have found that many organizations are using no tools or are attempting the advanced tools without knowing the basics of brainstorming, or when to use Pareto charts and simple tracking sheets. The intent of the tools described in this book, along with the five-step problem-solving process and the corrective and preventive action processes, is to give teams a structured approach. Each step of the problem-solving process is fully described with practice activities and skill builders, which allows readers to transfer the knowledge they gain from the chapters to their own current situation, thus reinforcing their level of understanding. A case study is also included, so that the reader can study the five-step problem-solving process through an entire problem.

Within this book, we have also included a chapter that discusses the concepts of continual improvement. While many people would agree that correcting problems permanently is the right thing to do, many would also agree that the process of achieving continual improvement in their organizations is poorly carried out or is missing all together. Much has been written about continual improvement and how to attain it. Some think that if only the right tool was used, if only management would supply more resources, if only the right program was implemented, then maybe the organization might see some evidence of continual improvement. Making continual improvement happen is more than selecting the right tool or providing the right amount of resources. It is an approach that requires the management team to collect and analyze meaningful data within the organization and use this information to make decisions and take actions to drive improvement.

Finally, we have written this book knowing the busy schedules and pressures that many of you have in trying to do your jobs, effectively solve problems, and implement improvements. It is our feeling that this book will be a basic road map to assist any organization looking for a way to improve!

1

Corrective and Preventive Action Overview

O n any given day in organizations all over the world, there are problems. These problems are reported by customers, suppliers, partners, employees, and so on. Many organizations send their employees out to deal with these problems as they occur. Even though these dedicated employees do their job and put out the fire, many of the same problems crop up again and the vicious cycle repeats itself over and over. Also, some organizations seem to be stuck in the corrective stage and do little in the way of prevention. In addition, numerous organizations struggle with applying the concepts of corrective and preventive action, as well as understanding how these two concepts fit into an effective problem-solving process.

PHILOSOPHY OF CORRECTIVE AND PREVENTIVE ACTION

The philosophy of corrective and preventive action has been part of the quality scene for over four decades. Several different quality gurus have promoted these concepts. Philip Crosby introduced the idea of prevention in his *second absolute of quality*, which was, "a system for causing quality is prevention." He also stated that prevention was causing something not to happen and that corrective action (which he introduced in his *14 steps of quality*) must be a systematic method set up by the organization to resolve problems forever. He indicated that the way this could be accomplished was through using measurements, cost of quality, quality improvement teams, management commitment, and quality awareness. He maintained that, in order to reduce costs, the organization needed to develop employees that would understand the whole job and troubleshoot the system for improvements at every stage.[1]

Joseph Juran introduced the concept of corrective and preventive action as part of the *Juran trilogy* under quality improvement. The philosophy behind the "trilogy" was that the organization must push beyond the established norm with operational quality in order to achieve superior performance. He stated that the quality improvement activities must include:

- An established infrastructure to ensure quality improvement that includes provision of resources and training for teams

- Specific projects that have been identified for improvement

- An established team with clear responsibility for successful closure of problem-solving activities

- Teams who are trained in:

  - Diagnosing causes

  - Establishing remedies

  - Holding gains through established controls[2]

Armand Feigenbaum also made prevention part of the quality equation. He established that there is an operating quality cost and that prevention costs (including quality planning), and other costs associated with preventing nonconformance and defects, were less than the costs of external failures reaching the customer. Crosby also emphasized the cost of quality by maintaining that "doing it right the first time" was less costly. He told management that while there are costs associated with preventing a situation, these costs are far less than those caused by errors.

W. Edwards Deming stated that errors and inconsistencies would always be a problem and that most of the time the "wrong" corrective action was applied. He recommended organizations have a methodology such as the Shewhart Cycle (plan–do–check–act) in order to analyze a problem.[3] Shewhart's plan–do–check–act was later modified by Deming and called the plan–do–study–act cycle, and is one of the most commonly used diagrams to describe the continual improvement process through a formalized method. This method provides the basis for many of the problem-solving methodologies used today.

The Difference between Corrective and Preventive Action

While the philosophies and concepts of corrective and preventive action have been around for a long time, it has always been a little murky as to how a problem-solving process should be established, and how both corrective and preventive action fit into this process. First, *corrective action* occurs as a result of a reported problem and is considered a reactive approach. Second, corrective action should be taken to eliminate the cause of existing problems, thus preventing them from recurring. Finally, corrective action should not be considered disciplinary action or a means in itself, but rather, part of the problem-solving process that analyzes issues with the intent of improving. It is important to note that the mere act of correcting a problem is different than taking corrective action. When correcting a problem, immediate action is taken which may or may not involve the additional steps of determining the root cause of the problem or following up for effectiveness. Correcting alone may not result in resolving the issue.

Conversely, *preventive action* is the response to information or knowledge that indicates that a potential problem might occur. This information or knowledge could come from trend analysis, risk analysis, market analysis, or previous experience. Using this information allows the organization to prevent the problem from happening in the first place.

Prevention of potential problems may require different thinking, since a preventive approach requires us to ask the "what-ifs." One way to start thinking about preventive action is to brainstorm the kinds of preventive actions that are experienced every day.

Take a few moments and list several examples of preventive actions you take at home and at work. Ask: If you didn't apply prevention, how much would it cost?

At Home:

At Work:

Some common examples of prevention at home are six-month dental checks, changing the oil in the car, planning menus before grocery shopping, alarm systems, smoke detectors, exercising, and eating healthy foods. Some common examples at work include training, preventive maintenance, verifications, checklists, safety equipment and procedures, developing goals and plans, and understanding customer requirements before a design is developed. Therefore, by thinking about the "what-ifs" and using previous knowledge and history, we reduce the likelihood that a problem will develop. Remember, addressing the prevention of potential problems is less costly then fixing them.

Corrective and Preventive Action Defined

The introduction of the ISO family of standards formalized the requirements of corrective and preventive action. However, confusion still surrounds these two concepts. One of the key reasons for this confusion is that, typically, corrective and preventive action are thought of as two steps of a problem-solving process. When thought of in this context, they are viewed as actions to be taken. In fact, this is the way *ANSI/ISO/ASQ Q9000:2005 Quality Management Systems—Fundamentals and Vocabulary* defines them:

> *Corrective action* is defined as an action taken to eliminate the cause of a detected non-conformity, which prevents the problem from recurring.

> *Preventive action* is defined as an action taken to eliminate the cause of a potential non-conformity from occurring.[4]

Corrective and Preventive Action As Processes

ANSI/ISO/ASQ Q9001:2008 not only defines corrective and preventive action as actions to be taken, but also lays out the basic foundation for a problem-solving process. Listed below is a description of the requirements of ANSI/ISO/ASQ Q9001:2008 for carrying out the corrective action process with a general description of each requirement.

ANSI/ISO/ASQ Q9001:2008 REQUIREMENTS

8.5.2 Corrective action

a) reviewing nonconformities (including customer complaints)

b) determining the causes of nonconformities

c) evaluating the need for action to ensure that nonconformities do not recur

d) determining and implementing action needed

e) records of the results of action taken

f) reviewing the effectiveness of the corrective action taken

a. *Reviewing identified problems to evaluate whether or not corrective action should take place.* When evaluating the need for action, it is important to consider the risk of the problem to the customers, employees, organization, and so on. Once this is decided, appropriate action can be taken based on the severity of that defined risk.

Many organizations make the mistake of sending every problem into a formal corrective and preventive action process, thus forcing them to investigate the cause of every issue. This can be costly and overwhelming to the organization. Therefore, every organization should consider having an intermediate step that allows them to prioritize their problems so that resources are not wasted on issues that have little impact on the organization or its customers.

b. *Determining why the problem happened.* The heart of an effective problem-solving process is identifying the true root cause of a problem. The "root" of the problem is the core issue that caused the problem to occur. Many times organizations identify a "symptom" of the problem as the root and, consequently, put ineffective actions in place without completing a full investigation. Only when the root is found can actions be taken to fix the problem for good.

c and d. *Evaluating and implementing the actions must be a planned event.* These steps of the problem-solving process are completed once the root cause has been determined. First, the need for actions is evaluated. Once the need for action has been determined, actions are developed and implemented. In the event that planned actions are not taken, it may become necessary to initiate an *escalation process.* Typically, this is when someone designated alerts a higher level of management that very little or no action has taken place. The expectation of this process is that management takes steps to get the plan moving again.

e. *Keeping records of the results.* Throughout the problem-solving process, good note taking is important. Sound records will provide a basis for whether or not the actions taken were effective. If complete notes are available from start to finish, those working on the problem will be able to revise their plan if the actions taken are not effective, without having to start all over again. Also, if trends indicate that the problem may be resurfacing, complete notes will help those who are investigating to understand what was done in the past.

f. *Checking the results of the actions taken.* This is one of the most critical parts of the whole process and is often not completed. Without it, organizations cannot determine if the actions that were implemented were effective in eliminating the problem. This follow-up is vitally important to the success of the problem-solving process. In fact, the process is not considered complete until the follow-up activities have occurred. In the event that the actions are ineffective, the investigation will need to be revisited.

PREVENTIVE ACTION

Taking corrective action and effectively applying problem solving with a thorough analysis of root cause is one way the organization can improve a situation after problems occur. Another way an organization can improve is to apply the concept of preventive action, which is taken before a situation develops. As was discussed earlier, preventive action is looking for potential causes. ANSI/ISO/ASQ Q9001:2008 defines the requirements of the preventive action process as follows:

8.5.3 Preventive action

a) determining potential nonconformities and their causes

b) evaluating the need for action to prevent occurrence of nonconformities

c) determining and implementing action needed

d) records of the results of action taken

e) reviewing the effectiveness of the preventive action taken

a. *Identify potential problems to prevent occurrence by analyzing the "what-ifs."* Identifying preventive action opportunities is based on analyzing and using information, typically trended over time. Causes of potential problems can be investigated by asking a question such as, "If this trend continues, is the likelihood high that it will cause a problem?" Management personnel are good candidates for reviewing this information, as they often have knowledge that gives them a full picture of the organization's activities, such as market development, product development, the financial picture, and resource needs. A good time to review this information is during management meetings when key indicators of the business are evaluated. Many organizations have reviews monthly, quarterly, or twice a year. If the organization has a quality management system and is meeting the requirements of ANSI/ISO/ASQ Q9001:2008, management can determine preventive action during management review.

b and c. *Evaluate the need for action, determine the action, and then implement.* As with corrective action, preventive action also requires evaluating the need for action. Once the need is established, the action must be determined and implemented. Dates and names should be assigned so that progress can be followed. It also may be advantageous to review previous records to see if similar issues have occurred in the past. This information may be helpful in deciding the course of action.

When determining if preventive action is needed, management should ask the following types of questions:

- Are we confident the data is accurate?

- If we don't do something now, how will it impact the customer? How will it impede our objectives? How will it impact the overall organization?

- What actions should be taken if the trends are positive?

- What actions should be taken if the trends are negative?

- What resources will be required? (For example, time, people, equipment.)

- How much money will it cost to implement the preventive action?

- Who will need to participate?

- When do we expect the action to be in place?

d. *Keep records for historical purposes.* Records should be kept of the preventive actions, including the results achieved. This will become the history of the activity and can be used by management for future reference.

e. *The results of the action must be checked.* As with corrective action, if preventive actions are initiated, someone should be in charge of following up to ensure that the action taken prevents the potential problem. This should take place at specified times by reviewing trends or other established measures to ensure the action was effective.

Many organizations are comfortable with initiating corrective action but less comfortable with the concept of preventive action. The concept of preventive action can be described in the following two ways:

1. *The end result of corrective action.* This approach is part of the problem-solving process that addresses root cause and ensures that

problems don't recur. In other words, if we do a good job at root cause analysis, we stop the problem and *prevent* it from recurring. (Refer to appendix A, which describes a generic corrective action process).

2. *Preventive action as a proactive approach.* These are actions taken based on analysis of information that eliminates the likelihood of a potential problem from occurring. This action can be taken one of two ways. First, before the completion of the problem-solving cycle, preventive action should be considered. Based on the corrective action that has been defined, the team determines if other areas in the organization are affected by the same problem. If so, they initiate preventive actions to ensure that those potential problems never occur. The other way to identify preventive action is using previous information or experience, therefore allowing action to be taken that will prevent problems from occurring in the first place. These actions may be taken by management based on trend analysis and/or other information coming from the organization. In organizations with ISO quality management systems, these decisions are typically made during the management review process. (Refer to appendix B, which describes a generic preventive action process).

Taking preventive action as a proactive approach is highly desirable, as it will reduce costs compared to spending time and dollars to fix a problem that has already upset the apple cart. Loss of dollars in terms of materials, customer satisfaction, human resources, and market share cannot be easily recouped once a major problem is allowed to develop. Therefore, preventing problems up front before they happen is where organizations need to spend their energy.

FINAL THOUGHT

In order to effectively implement corrective and preventive action, organizations must take steps that will both resolve an issue and prevent it from coming back. Furthermore, the concept of prevention needs to be understood so that the organization not only applies it to the end result of corrective action in terms of preventing recurrence, but also thinks beyond this application and looks at prevention to ensure that potential problems don't occur. As Philip Crosby once said, *Why spend all this time finding and fixing and fighting when you could have prevented the problem in the first place?*

2

Getting Started with the Problem-Solving Process

What is a problem? A problem is an undesirable deviation from an expected desirable outcome. In other words, something went wrong! Where do problems come from?

Problems can flow into the organization from many different avenues. Unfortunately, some organizations keep a myopic view in that the only problems that are identified and investigated for root cause are found during internal or external audits. This type of thinking results in limitations for the organization in its quest for continual improvement through missed opportunities. Other sources where problems may come from include:

- Customer complaints and satisfaction data

- Product nonconformances

- Management review

- Process measurements

- Product measurements

- Customer returns

- Warranty issues

- Supplier problems

- Trended information

- Risk analysis

- Market analysis

- Employee surveys

By recognizing the many sources from which problems or potential problems can be discovered, the organization widens its view and increases its chance for improvement.

Another way organizations can increase their chances for improvement is by understanding the difference between the cause of a problem and the symptom of a problem. While problem-solving methods, including the corrective and preventive action processes of ANSI/ISO/ASQ Q9001:2008, focus on elimination of cause, many organizations mistakenly implement actions based on the identification of a symptom rather than the cause. When this happens, actions are put into place that don't stop the problem. What is the difference between a symptom and a cause?

SYMPTOM OR CAUSE?

Many of us pride ourselves in how efficient we are at solving problems. It is not uncommon to hear one boast: "There. It's fixed!" Fixing what is broken or perceived to be broken is second nature to human beings. Webster defines a problem as:

A question proposed for solution or consideration; a question, matter or situation that is perplexing or difficult; a problem may have multiple symptoms.

The last part of Webster's definition is important. Very often, the reason problems are resolved unsatisfactorily is that the symptoms are treated instead of the cause. By treating the symptom, we end up solving the wrong issue. One of the first things that must be understood is the difference between a symptom and a cause.

A symptom is defined as:

Any circumstance, event, or condition that accompanies something and indicates its existence or occurrence; a sign.

A cause is defined as:

A situation or event that produces an effect or result.

Sometimes, deciding whether or not we are looking at a symptom or a cause is not so easy. Problem-solving teams who are in a hurry to "just fix it" will invariably find they are attempting to solve a symptom rather than identifying and eliminating the true root cause.

In order to further understand the differences between symptom and cause, study the checklist below. Items on this list are often found with many problems. Using a problem from work, check off "Yes" or "No" to the symptoms that apply.

Symptom	Yes	No
Lack of understanding		
Missing information		
Inaccurate information		
Incomplete information		
Procedures are incomplete or missing		
People don't know how to do it		
Procedures are not followed		
No follow-through		
Lack of training		
Employee error		
Equipment failure		
Customer complaints		
Process is not defined		

How many symptoms applied to the problem you identified? What would happen if corrective action were applied to one of the symptoms you identified instead of the actual cause of the problem? How many resources would be wasted? Would the problem come back?

As you can see, it is important to determine whether or not you are looking at symptoms or causes. Coming up with a solution based on the symptom rather than the cause wastes resources.

One way to determine if you are addressing the symptom instead of the cause is to test the symptom with a question. For instance, if "lack of understanding" was a symptom, you could ask, "Why do we have lack of understanding?" In this example, the "why" question leaves the symptom open for more questioning, moving you closer to the cause. To further understand this technique, let's imagine that "procedures not followed" is the problem. In order to test whether or not we have identified a symptom or cause, we need to apply the "why" method. Usually if "why" is asked *at least five times*, the likelihood that the real cause has been found will be greater.

Question	Answer
1. Why aren't procedures followed?	1. Procedures are not available.
2. Why aren't the procedures available?	2. They were revised and not returned to the department.
3. Why weren't they returned to the department?	3. The new documentation coordinator didn't know he was responsible.
4. Why didn't he know he was responsible?	4. He didn't complete his training.
5. Why didn't he complete his training?	5. His manager didn't notify him of the training class.

In the above example, even more questions can be asked, such as, why didn't the manager notify him? By drilling down into the symptoms, you come closer to finding out what really caused the problem. Your problem solving would take a different path if you had taken action on the first answer as opposed to the last answer to the "why" question. The symptom, "not following procedures," is only a sign or event that is accompanying the true problem.

GETTING STARTED

Many organizations have already established some type of problem-solving methodology. Whether it's Shewart's PDCA cycle, or a five-, six-, or seven-step process, the important thing to remember is that a formalized approach is necessary for effective problem solving. The problem-solving process need not be complicated. To keep things simple, this book describes a *five-step problem-solving process*. The five steps are:

1. Describe the problem.

2. Investigate the cause.

3. Select and test solutions.

4. Implement the solutions.

5. Verify and monitor the solutions.

Refer to appendix C for a table that describes each step.

In addition, it is important to clarify the connection between the ANSI/ISO/ASQ Q9001:2008 requirements and the problem-solving process, as shown in Table 2.1.

Table 2.1   Connecting ANSI/ISO/ASQ Q9001:2008 to problem solving.

ANSI/ISO/ASQ Q9001:2008 Requirements	5-Step Problem-Solving Process
8.5.2 Corrective action	
a) reviewing nonconformities (including customer complaints)	Step 1: Describe the Problem
b) determining the causes of nonconformities	Step 2: Investigate the Cause
c) evaluating the need for action to ensure that nonconformities do not recur	Step 3: Select and Test Solutions
d) determining and implementing action needed	Step 4: Implement the Solutions
e) records of the results of action taken	Step 4: Implement the Solutions Step 5: Verify and Monitor the Solutions
f) reviewing the effectiveness of the corrective action taken	Step 5: Verify and Monitor the Solutions
8.5.3 Preventive action	
a) determining potential nonconformities and their causes	Step 1: Describe the Problem Step 2: Investigate the Cause
b) evaluating the need for action to prevent occurrence of nonconformities	Step 3: Select and Test Solutions
c) determining and implementing action needed	Step 4: Implement the Solutions
d) records of the results of action taken	Step 4: Implement the Solutions Step 5: Verify and Monitor the Solutions
e) reviewing the effectiveness of the preventive action taken	Step 5: Verify and Monitor the Solutions

As was mentioned before, any number of steps may be used in problem solving. The important thing to remember is that resolving problems and eliminating them from coming back requires a process, and every step in that process must be completed, from describing the problem through verifying the effectiveness of the implemented actions. There are no shortcuts in an effective problem-solving process. Problem solving takes time and resources. Therefore, it is imperative that good decisions are made as to which problems will go full cycle through the problem-solving process and which ones will be tracked for further evaluation. This decision begins at the point of the "fast fix."

The Fast Fix

When a problem occurs, a "fast fix" may be put into place. Plugging the dam is the starting point in the problem-solving process. Putting a fast fix into place may be necessary to get the job to the customer and continue operations. This is the point where many organizations stop, therefore creating the firefighting mode. At this juncture, a decision needs to be made as to whether or not a full investigation should take place. How do you make the decision? Fix the problem and move on when the problem is a one-time occurrence with minimal risk. In other words, if the costs to the organization are not high, and this is not a recurring event, then looking for the root cause will not warrant the resources for a full-blown problem-solving activity.

However, you may want to track these one-time occurrences to ensure that they aren't the start of a bigger problem. It is sometimes helpful to sort issues or problems into buckets. One bucket would represent low risk, one-time occurrences that can be tracked for future evaluation. The other bucket would represent problems that meet certain criteria established by the organization and require full investigation. Another way to think about this type of prioritization is called the "triage approach."

The Triage Approach

If you have ever been to an emergency room for a non–life threatening injury, you probably had to wait hours and hours for assistance. That is because personnel in emergency rooms practice the "triage" approach. That is, as each person comes in, the hospital personnel first determine how severe the situation is. Once this has been established, they send the person to the right location, such as the waiting room, a hospital bed, or the operating room. Without this approach, the emergency room would be clogged with ineffective and inefficient services. Furthermore, this approach allows the hospital staff to prioritize their problems (the injured people) and determine immediate action (the fast fix).

The same analogy can be used for an organization's problem-solving process, including its corrective and preventive action system. Many organizations find themselves with overloaded corrective and preventive action systems with too many entries in a database or on a log sheet that someone is required to track. In this situation, every problem is deemed urgent, thus requiring investigation and action. When this happens, time is wasted on fixing the "trivial many" rather than the "vital few."

In order to establish a triage approach, organizations must first develop criteria for what constitutes a problem and requires a full investigation. These criteria must then be communicated to pertinent personnel so that it is clear when the problem-solving process should be started. The following list provides examples of criteria when root cause should be investigated:

- The customer discovers the problem. Keep in mind that when the customer discovers the problem, your internal processes have failed. This includes both service and product issues.

- Significant dollar loss occurs. You need to decide what is classified as a significant amount.

- The problem has a history of recurring. (Negative trends are evident.)

- Risk is high in losing the customer.

- Safety is jeopardized.

- Product quality has been impacted and product must be scrapped.

- Product defects are discovered at the end of the line, indicating the process has failed.

- Internal and external audit findings indicate repeated problems.

- The customer initiates a request for explanation of root cause.

Without established criteria for what types of issues should go into the problem-solving process, the number of problems that people think requires analysis will be overwhelming. Laying this foundation first will help channel resources to the most significant issues. A Pareto chart can be used to graphically depict the most significant issues.[1] This chart enables the organization to focus on the "vital few" that need further investigation. Furthermore, this chart can be used to rank the importance of the issues so that time is not wasted on problems with minimal impact to the organization.

FINAL THOUGHT

Problems can come from many sources. Dealing effectively with problems requires that organizations understand the differences between symptoms and causes. By quickly jumping to conclusions, symptoms often are identified as causes, leading the organization down the wrong path to eliminating the issue. In order to get started with effective problem solving, the organization needs to develop a formalized approach and ensure that every step of the problem-solving methodology is completed. It also requires that they have methods in place to prioritize issues so that resources aren't wasted by applying root cause analysis to every problem.

3
Step 1: Describe the Problem

A problem well-defined is a problem half-solved.

—Anonymous

The first step in the problem-solving process is to ensure that the description of the problem is stated in clear, specific terms without drawing conclusions or making assumptions. This provides the starting point. Without a clear definition of the situation, the problem-solving team will likely start with the wrong information, thus leading to the possibility that the problem will not be eliminated for good.

In order to clearly define the problem, information needs to be collected. At this point, the focus should be on the information, not the solution. A handy tool for defining the problem is the 4W/2H/1C formula. By using this formula, the problem can be defined in terms of *what, where, when, who, how* much, *how* often, and the *consequences.*

When reviewing the problem, specific questions should be asked (see Figure 3.1).

Keep in mind that if the customer has identified the problem, the problem should be defined from the customer's viewpoint. In other words, how do they see it? Many times teams attempt to solve problems from their own viewpoint without regard for the customer. When this happens, the implemented solution might not solve the problem. The better approach is to gather as much information from the customer as possible before the team defines the problem.

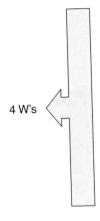

4 W's

1. What was affected? *Be specific about which job numbers, part numbers, customers, and so on, were affected.*

2. Where did the problem take place? *Be specific about where the problem was found, that is, department, equipment, customer, and so on.*

3. When was the problem discovered? *Was it discovered at the end of the production run, on a certain shift, and so on?*

4. Who discovered the problem? *Was it discovered internally or by the customer?*

2 H's

1. How much was affected? *Think in terms of number of orders, amount of product, number of dollars, number of customers, and so on.*

2. How often has this problem occurred? *Is this the first time or has the same or similar issue happened in the past?*

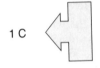

1 C

1. What is the consequence of this situation? *Did the customer receive a late shipment, or were other orders late because of the situation, and so on?*

Figure 3.1   The 4W/2H/1C formula.

For example, a customer saying "the product doesn't work" will not give a problem-solving team enough information to define the problem. In some organizations, when the customer says "the product doesn't work," the problem-solving team will jump immediately to reasons why this occurred, without ever collecting enough information. Instead, the team should address the 4W/2H/1C formula with the customer in order to accurately describe the problem. Without doing this critical first step, a lot of time, money, and energy will be spent chasing the wrong problem.

Listed in Table 3.1 is an example of how the 4W/2H/1C formula can be used to identify the specifics in order to clearly describe the problem.

Table 3.1   Using the 4W/2H/1C formula.

	Question	Answer
W	What was affected?	Part #XJC3589
W	Where did the problem take place?	At the Texas facility
W	When was the problem discovered?	On 8/15/08 @ 3:15pm (first shift)
W	Who discovered the problem?	Jack Smith—Line A operator
H	How much was affected?	47 units with the same problem on Line A
H	How often has this problem occurred?	First time occurrence—no previous record
C	What is the consequence of this situation?	375 units on hold in finished goods inventory; No in-process units; customer has 187 units on hold at their location. Customer is suspending all future orders until problem is resolved.

PROBLEM DESCRIPTION

Nonconforming part #XJC3589 was found at the Texas facility on first shift by a Line A operator on 8/15/08 at 3:15 PM. Forty-seven units of the same product with the same problem were also found on Line A. No defective in-process units found. This is a first-time occurence. 375 units were put on hold in the finished goods inventory and the customer has also put 187 units on hold at their location. The customer is suspending all future orders until the problem is resolved.

FINAL THOUGHT

Clearly defining the problem is an important step in effective problem solving. Unfortunately, many organizations attempt to take action from their problem description without applying the 4W/2H/1C formula. This results in actions being taken on vague, incomplete, or inaccurate information that might only identify the symptom of the problem. The first course of action is for the team to analyze the description and make the determination if additional information is needed. Once the description is clearly stated, the plan for investigation can be developed and effective problem solving can begin.

REVIEW

Step 1
Describe the Problem

1. Focus on the information that is known. Do not think about the solution.

2. Be specific about the situation. Use the 4W/2H/1C formula to answer:

   - What was affected?

   - When did it happen?

   - Where did it happen?

   - Who discovered it?

   - How much was affected?

   - How often has it happened?

   - What is the consequence?

3. By including the consequence, the situation becomes real in terms of the impact to the customer and the organization.

4. Clarification of the description of the problem prevents confusion and jumping to conclusions.

Practice Session

To better understand how to use the 4W/2H/1C formula, review the following situations and determine whether or not the team has clearly defined the problem. Have all the necessary questions been answered? If needed, at the end of each section, add the information required by the 4W/2H/1C formula that should be included.

Problem A:

The procedures were not followed for final inspection. Full inspection of the parts is required. The operator only did a partial inspection.

Problem B:

The change orders are not being reviewed and signed by the sales department. Several change orders were found in production without authorization. The operators were confused about the changes and out-of-spec parts were produced.

Examples of How to Use the 4W/2H/1C Formula for Problems A and B

Problem A

The procedures were not followed for final inspection. Full inspection of the parts is required. The operator only did a partial inspection.

	Question	Answer
W	What was affected?	Parts #F1347H were not inspected according to procedure
W	Where did the problem take place?	Paint department
W	When was the problem discovered?	On 11/10/08 third shift
W	Who discovered the problem?	Ken Lesser—quality department
H	How much was affected?	265 parts
H	How often has this problem occurred?	Previous records show that the problem has occurred in March, June, and August, 2008.
C	What is the consequence of this situation?	Parts were scrapped. Customer's order was delayed by 10 days.

Problem B

The change orders are not being reviewed and signed by the sales department. Several change orders were found in production without authorization. The operators were confused about the changes and out-of-spec parts were produced.

	Question	Answer
W	What was affected?	Change orders # 56748, 76987, 56321, 59897, were not authorized.
W	Where did the problem take place?	Sales department
W	When was the problem discovered?	10/12/08
W	Who discovered the problem?	Mary Kim—planning department
H	How much was affected?	Four jobs equivalent of $375,000 were put on hold. 50% of job 56748-003 was scrapped.
H	How often has this problem occurred?	Problem has occurred nine times this month.
C	What is the consequence of this situation?	Four jobs listed above were put on hold and part of one job had to be destroyed. Customer delivery dates were not met.

Skill Builder

Practice analyzing descriptions of past problems found in your organization. Use the 4W/2H/1C formula to determine if these problems have been described in specific terms. If not, what is missing? In your opinion, how would a completed description have changed the solution to the problem?

4

Step 2: Investigate
the Cause

How many 'fixes' backfire because the assumptions on which the fix was based turn out to be false?

—Murgatroyd and Morgan

Once the problem has been clearly described, it is time for investigating the "root cause" of the problem. Root cause analysis is a structured approach for finding the real reason the problem occurred. As mentioned earlier, rather than finding the root cause, organizations instead often identify a symptom of the problem as the root and, subsequently, implement a solution that will not work. Finding the root cause takes people, time, patience, and tools. If the investigative stage is done right, the team will most likely spend the largest amount of time on this step (see Figure 4.1).

HOW TO START

Before an investigation begins, the following factors should be considered:

• *Get the right people in the room.* Make use of experience and expertise with a team of people, including the owners of the process (those who may need to change their practices), where the problem is occurring. Other technical experts, as well as the recipients of the output of the process in question, may also need to be included. Telling just one person to go "fix it" does not work. More often than not, the collective intelligence of a team of people will more quickly solve a problem. Team members will need to be

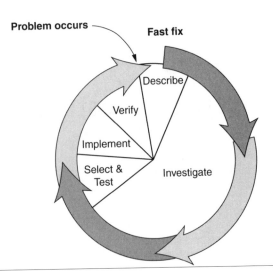

Figure 4.1 Time spent in the problem-solving process.

familiar with skills for problem solving, meeting basics, and team dynamics. For more on teams, see chapter 9, "Importance of Effective Teams in the Problem-Solving Process."

• *Use proven root cause analysis tools.* Some basic tools for determining root cause analysis include flowcharts, brainstorming, cause-and-effect diagrams, the 5 Whys, and Pareto charts. While many more tools are available, these tools provide a basic foundation to begin the problem-solving process. More information can be found in chapter 8, "Basic Problem-Solving Tools."

• *Think "out-of-the-box."* Do not limit thinking by stating what has always been done. Be creative. When brainstorming, don't be afraid to write down the most outrageous or silly idea. This prevents the team from shutting down and keeps the channels open to all possibilities.

• *Take the time needed.* Problems that are solved in a hurry are never solved for good. When more time is spent up front to solve problems so that they never occur again, less time will be needed for reacting to the same problems over and over. Ultimately, organizations should spend their time looking for ways to prevent problems from ever occurring in the first place.

• *Put a plan together.* Developing an investigation plan sets the process in motion and keeps the team from jumping into solutions before the cause has been identified.

DEVELOPING THE PLAN

If the team does not have a lot of experience in problem-solving activities or has not been successful in executing the problem-solving process quickly, developing a plan can help formalize the team's starting point. The plan does not need to be elaborate, but should capture some essential information. This information will assist the team in determining whether or not they need to collect more data before they begin any formal brainstorming activities.

Figure 4.2 is an example of an *investigation action plan checklist*.

Investigation Action Plan Checklist	
Describe the fast fix that was taken (if applicable):	
Is the fix working at the moment? (If not, explain what will be done in the short term.)	Yes
	No
List the owner of the problem: List those who need to be involved:	
List information currently available to assist in the investigation: Data: Employee input: Flowcharts of the process: Procedures: Records including SPC charts, measurements, and other quantitative data:	
Has the problem occurred in the past? Yes/No If yes, what records exist?	
Frequency of meetings: (daily, weekly, etc.) Time: Place: First meeting date:	

Figure 4.2   Investigation action plan checklist.

Once the correct team has been assembled and a plan has been developed, the investigation can begin. Although there are a variety of approaches to root cause analysis, the following steps constitute a basic approach:

1. Identify the potential causes of the problem. This can be done by:

   - Generating a cause-and effect diagram

   - Analyzing process flowcharts

   - Discussing the problem with individuals that have expertise in that area

   - Analyzing records and other quantitative data, such as SPC charts and other measurements

2. Select the most likely of causes:

   - Utilize collective knowledge and expertise.

   - Eliminate causes that have no likelihood of creating the problem.

3. Evaluate the possible causes as the root:

   - Determine how a possible cause could have created the problem.

   - Decide on data needed to prove or disprove a potential cause.

4. Collect and analyze data for the possible causes:

   - Break into smaller teams to investigate likely causes at the same time.

   - Interview appropriate personnel.

   - Try to re-create the problem.

   - Look at records to help pinpoint the problem.

5. Select the cause that is the root:

   - Document the information that confirms that the selected cause is the root.

   - Demonstrate that the root cause created the problem.

   - Confirm that the root cause addresses the description of the problem.

Once the team has finalized the root cause, they are ready to move to the next step, which is selecting and testing the solution.

FINAL THOUGHT

Adequate time will need to be allocated to the investigative step in order to effectively identify the root cause. This step should not be rushed, and the team should ensure that enough data and/or information is available about the problem before determining the root cause. A simple plan of action will keep the team focused and will identify if additional legwork is needed before brainstorming begins. The team should at least have some team members who understand how to effectively use problem-solving tools.

REVIEW

Step 2
Investigate the Cause

1. Develop an investigation plan.

2. Determine person(s) to be involved.

3. Use tools to help determine the root cause, such as:

    a. Brainstorming

    b. Data gathering

    c. Interviews

    d. Cause-and-effect diagram

    e. Other

4. Determine the root cause.

Practice Session

Analyze the root causes that are described below for the problem descriptions you reviewed from the previous chapter. Both the description and root cause are listed. Does the root cause appear to address the description? What is missing? Do you think addressing the root cause will eliminate the problem?

Problem A:

Description: The procedures were not followed for final inspection. Full inspection of the parts is required. The operator only did a partial inspection.

Root Cause: Operator error. Lack of training.

Problem B:

Description: The change orders are not being reviewed and signed by the sales department. Several change orders were found in production without authorization. The operators were confused about the changes and out-of-spec parts were produced.

Root Cause: A written procedure was not followed. New employees, or lack of training and accountability, may be part of the problem.

Problem A

Description. The procedures were not followed for final inspection. Full inspection of the parts is required. The operator only did a partial inspection.

Root Cause. Operator error. Lack of training.

Discussion. The root cause identified is most likely not the cause. For instance, if the "5 Whys" are applied to this cause, more questions could be asked. Why was there lack of training? Did someone forget to do the training? Is there no formal process for training? Was the training done, but not effective? The team should do more investigation on this problem to ensure that they have exhausted all possibilities.

Problem B

Description. The change orders are not being reviewed and signed by the sales department. Several change orders were found in production without authorization. The operators were confused about the changes and out-of-spec parts were produced.

Root Cause. A written procedure was not followed. New employees, or lack of training and accountability, may be a part of the problem.

Discussion. The root cause appears to be incomplete and the additional reasons stated by the team indicate they are unsure. Why do they think that new employees, training, and accountability may be part of the problem? Why was the procedure not followed? Is the procedure too complex? Does the procedure incorrectly define the process that should be followed?

Again, the team needs to exhaust all of the possibilities and drill down into the issue to determine the root cause.

Skill Builder

Practice analyzing root causes of past problems found in your organization. Compare the causes to the problem descriptions. In your opinion, did addressing the root cause resolve the issue? Look at several problems that have occurred in the last two months. Have similar problems occurred? How many times does the same root cause appear? The same root cause being used over and over (for example, lack of training, operator error, and so on) may indicate that the root cause has not been found.

5

Step 3: Select and Test Solutions

The difference between ordinary and extraordinary is that little extra.

—Anonymous

The next step in problem solving is to generate and select the most likely solutions, and to decide whether or not the solutions need to be tested. Based on the root cause, the team will need to decide what type of solution will be needed in order to eliminate the problem.

In order to determine the best solution, the following steps should be followed:

1. Brainstorm potential solutions:

   • For instance, if "no packaging criteria" is the root cause, ask: "If criteria were developed, would they prevent recurrence? Why?"

2. Assess the impact to the system:

   • What is the size of the problem? If the problem were resolved, would the benefit to the organization be greater than the resources that were spent? How would the solution impact the rest of the system? (That is, this department, the department in front of or behind the process.)

3. Select the most likely of solutions (there may be more than one):

   • Does the proposed solution need to be tested on a smaller scale? If so, ask, what is the plan?

- Which department will the proposed solution be tested in?

- How long will it be tested?

- Who will need to know the test plan and the results?

The team will need to come to consensus as to the best solution(s) for the problem. The key question for the team is whether or not the solution will prevent recurrence. It is important to realize that problem solving is not an exact science, but theoretical. The proposed solution is usually based on a combination of facts, previous knowledge, and experience. Therefore, analyzing the impact of the solution on the processes and/or the entire system and testing the proposed solution will help the team be more precise in taking corrective action that will prevent recurrence. The selection and testing step of the problem-solving process is an opportunity for the team to test their theory and even to change their game plan if the theory proves wrong. Furthermore, it is more cost-effective to find out the theory doesn't work early on than to go through a full-blown implementation.

IMPACT ANALYSIS

An impact analysis includes more than determining how much the proposed solution will cost. When a solution has been identified, the team can analyze the impact their proposal will have, as shown in Figure 5.1. If any of the categories evoke a negative response, the team may want to rethink their strategy. If all the analysis looks positive, the team should ask the following questions as a final check:

1. Does the solution look logical for the root cause?

2. Does the solution appear to be something that can realistically be implemented?

3. Does it appear that the solution is the best option and could prevent recurrence?

Once the team reaches consensus, the next step is to determine the method of testing the solution(s). Depending on the problem, this can be done within a department, within a specific process, on a certain shift, on a certain product, and so on. The purpose of the test(s) is to verify whether or not the proposed solution is the right one. Testing may not need to be done on every problem, but is especially helpful when multiple solutions have been identified or there is great risk to the customer if the solution fails. An example where testing may not be needed would be when the root

Impact Analysis			
Root Cause:			
Proposed Solution(s):			
Analysis	**How will the solution impact the system?**	**Positive** ✓	**Negative** ✓
Cost			
Safety			
Product			
Process/System			
Customer			
Supplier			

Key:

1. *Cost:* What will the solution cost? (Include materials, wages, equipment, etc.)
2. *Safety Issues:* Will anyone be put in jeopardy because of this solution?
3. *Product Issues:* Will the product still meet spec?
4. *Process/System Issues:* Will other processes or systems be negatively affected? Will there be a compliance issue if the solution is implemented?
5. *Customer:* Will they still get what they want?
6. *Supplier:* Can the supplier remain the same?

Figure 5.1   Impact analysis.

cause identifies a softer skill issue, such as the manager forgetting to inform the employee, thus the solution may be to clarify and revisit the person's role as a manager. While the person's performance could be monitored over time, it would be difficult to test this solution before it was implemented. The team will need to decide whether or not testing is appropriate for the root cause.

DETERMINING ACTIONS FOR SOLUTIONS

When determining corrective actions, it is important that the organization have a structured problem-solving approach. Without a structured approach, actions are usually developed quickly and without much thought. The following list is a few examples of actual corrective actions that have been identified by organizations. While these actions are well-intended, they will most likely not prevent the problem from coming back. Do any of these sound familiar?

- Sent more product to the customer

- More training needed

- Issued credit to the customer

- Apologized to the customer

- Fired the operator

- Human error

Just as the root cause analysis process requires a team of people, determining effective corrective actions that are based on prevention requires a cross-functional approach. The expertise from different individuals is invaluable when trying to develop the best action(s) to eliminate the problem. Since some actions might require more money, more time, or more people, it is important to have the right people on the team that might know the feasibility of the proposed actions. It will be a waste of time to put actions down that are really a "wish list." Instead, the team should focus on the actions that are feasible and that will fix the problem and prevent it from happening again. Sometimes, organizations may need to choose the less desirable solution because they are limited in resources. When this happens, the organization can only minimize the problem rather than solve it permanently.

When determining actions for the solutions, organizations should ask themselves:

- How will the actions affect the customer?

- Will the actions negatively affect other processes within the organization?

- How much will it cost to implement the actions?

- Do we have the necessary resources?

- How long will it take?

- Who is going to do it?

- Due to limited resources, will we need to implement a short-term solution while planning for a more permanent one?

FINAL THOUGHT

A proposed solution is a theory based on facts, previous knowledge, and experience. Selecting a solution will require some analysis. Using a tool like impact analysis (Figure 5.1) found in this chapter can help the team to assess the overall impact of the proposed solution on the rest of the system. Once the team has decided on a solution and is ready to test their theory, they will put together a plan for implementing the test following the same steps as if the test were a "live" implementation. The selection and test step is critical to ensure that the proposed solution prevents recurrence of the problem and is implemented effectively.

REVIEW

Step 3
Select and Test Solutions

1. Brainstorm potential solutions. Do we *think* the proposed solution will prevent recurrence? Why?

2. Assess the impact on the system. What is the size of the problem? If the problem is resolved, will the benefit to the organization be greater than the resources that were spent?

3. Select the most likely of solutions (there may be more than one):

   a. Do we need to test the proposed solution on a smaller scale?

   b. What is the plan? (Steps will be the same as the implementation phase but on a smaller scale.)

   c. Which department will the proposed solution be tested in?

   d. How long will it be tested?

   e. Who will need to know?

4. Select the "best" solution.

Practice Session

Analyze the solution that was selected. In your opinion, does the solution fit the root cause? Does the solution appear to be one that will prevent recurrence? Why or why not?

Problem A:

Description: The procedures were not followed for final inspection. Full inspection of the parts is required. The operator only did a partial inspection.

Root Cause: Operator error. Lack of training.

Action to Be Taken: Retrain operator when next classes are offered.

Problem B:

Description: The change orders are not being reviewed and signed by the Sales department. Several change orders were found in production without authorization. The operators were confused about the changes and out-of-spec parts were produced.

Root Cause: A written procedure was not followed. New employees, or lack of training and accountability, may be part of the problem.

Action to Be Taken: Rewrite procedure so it is easier to understand. Review accountability with new hires. Conduct training by end of month.

Problem A

Description. The procedures were not followed for final inspection. Full inspection of the parts is required. The operator only did a partial inspection.

Root Cause. Operator error. Lack of training.

Action to Be Taken. Retrain operator when next classes are offered.

Discussion. As was discussed in the previous chapter, the root cause needed more research since too many questions were left unanswered. Therefore, the solution that was selected most likely will not prevent the issue from coming back. Also, the solution does not clarify the specifics, such as what classes will be taken and when they will be completed, which creates guesswork as to whether or not the solution was implemented, thus impeding efforts to verify effectiveness.

Problem B

Description. The change orders are not being reviewed and signed by the sales department. Several change orders were found in production without authorization. The operators were confused about the changes and out-of-spec parts were produced.

Root Cause. A written procedure was not followed. New employees, or lack of training and accountability, may be part of the problem.

Action to Be Taken. Rewrite procedure so it is easier to understand. Review accountability with new hires. Conduct training by end of month.

Discussion. It is not clear how rewriting the procedure will ensure that the procedure is followed in the future. Also, what impact will a rewrite have on other processes? Again, because the cause doesn't appear to be fully investigated, the team is coming up with a solution that may or may not work. Did they determine whether or not the proposed solution was the best option that could prevent recurrence? What other solutions did they brainstorm? What causes them to think that the training is only needed for new hires? Should the rewrite to the procedure be tested before it is fully implemented?

Skill Builder

Analyze solutions to problems found in your organization. In your opinion, do the solutions appear to be well thought out? Have they prevented recurrence of problems? Were tests done? What were the results?

6

Step 4: Implement the Solutions

Once the team reaches the implementation step, much work has been done to identify the root cause, test the theories, and select solution(s). The implementation step formalizes the activities that will take place in order to carry out the identified corrective and preventive action(s). In order to implement the actions that have been determined, the team must be very clear in identifying who is going to do what by when. Without a defined list of actions, owners, and due dates, implementation may have a slim chance for success. Some organizations struggle with managing actions and due dates because they do not use a standardized format to record information. A *problem resolution report* is listed in appendix D as an example. Many organizations that have implemented corrective and preventive action processes through the ISO standards may have similar forms that help them to manage these activities.

When developing the corrective and preventive action implementation plan, the following factors should be considered:

- What are the actions?

- Who is the owner of each one?

- Who is going to implement each one?

- When will each one be completed?

- How will each action be verified for effectiveness?

- Will documentation need to be changed?

- Will people need to be trained?

- Has material that is in process, in stock, or at the customer's been affected?

- Are design changes needed?

- Does new tooling need to be made?

- If the customer will be impacted, by when and how much?

- Are there safety issues to consider?

The implementation step is also the time to decide on the plan for verifying the actions taken. What verification methods will be used? Who will carry them out? When will they be completed? If monitoring is decided upon, what is the frequency? More about verification and monitoring is discussed in chapter 7, "Step 5: Verify and Monitor the Solutions."

RECORDING THE IMPLEMENTATION ACTION PLAN

Many organizations record the root cause but fail to record the actions that are needed to successfully carry out the implementation plan. Poorly carried out plans can give the appearance that the team didn't do its job in identifying the root cause or the actions. Furthermore, a well-planned implementation can mean the difference between a successful resolution to a problem and one that falls short of preventing recurrence. A simple checklist can do the trick in ensuring that the team hasn't forgotten to communicate to certain individuals or trained those who will implement the actions. This record also adds to the history of the actions that was taken. This checklist can be part of the minute-keeping or be located on the problem-solving form. Figure 6.1 is an example of how a checklist might look.

Tracking the Status of Corrective and Preventive Actions

Once the implementation plan has been developed, it should stay on someone's radar screen while the actions are being carried out. In other words, keep track of the actions, owners, and due dates. Don't let things slip through the cracks or the implementation will not take place and the problem will creep up again! Depending on how many corrective and preventive actions are being managed, the organization will need to decide the best way to track them. Databases and spreadsheets are common methods. Smaller organizations may be able to track their progress manually.

Implementation Checklist		
Task	**Due Date**	**Person Assigned**
Who does the solution need to be communicated to? Brainstorm all those who need to be informed. Include customer, if needed.		
When does the communication need to take place? List the date, who will do it, and the method.		
Is training needed? List who needs to be trained, who will conduct it, and the date of completion.		
Do procedures need to be modified? List numbers and when they need to be implemented.		
Develop the plan for follow-up verification activities. Include frequency, methods, and persons responsible.		

Figure 6.1　Implementation checklist.

The status of corrective and preventive actions should be monitored at least monthly to ensure that due dates are on track. For organizations with ISO 9001 quality management systems, the status of corrective and preventive action is an input requirement for management review meetings. The purpose of the management review is to analyze data about the quality management system. Information about corrective and preventive actions should be compiled into a format or report to help management identify trends. This reporting can also help management to remove any roadblocks and to ensure that the actions are handled in a timely manner.

FINAL THOUGHT

Once teams reach the implementation step, the bulk of the work in determining the best possible solution has been completed. However, the work that needs to be done during the implementation phase should not be underestimated. One of the most important parts of the implementation step is to ensure that those individuals affected or involved receive communication and, where appropriate, training. Doing this will prevent a poorly executed implementation plan. Also, if procedure modifications are needed, they should be implemented at this time to ensure that personnel are working with the most current documentation. Finally, the plan for follow-up and verification activities should be determined.

REVIEW

Step 4
Implement the Solutions

1. Plan and record the implementation of the actions:

   a. When will they be implemented?

   b. What departments will be affected?

   c. Will the customer be impacted?

2. Has the solution been communicated to everyone, including management, operators, customer, and so on?

3. Have the verification methods been planned for to ensure follow-up after the implementation?

4. Will procedures or processes need to be modified?

   a. Who will be responsible to modify?

   b. When will they be completed?

5. Will people need to be trained?

   a. Who will conduct the training?

   b. When will the training need to be completed?

Skill Builder

Review previous corrective and preventive actions that have been implemented in your organization. What type of plan was used, if any, to successfully implement the actions? Was the plan documented and communicated to appropriate personnel? Did the implementation appear to be successful? Why or why not?

7

Step 5: Verify and Monitor the Solutions

VERIFICATION

Verifying the solutions is critical to the success of eliminating problems for good. This step focuses on whether or not the implemented corrective and preventive actions worked. If these actions are not verified by some means, how can the organization be sure that the problem won't appear down the road?

When developing verification plans, consider the following factors:

- Who will verify the actions? (may be internal auditors or similar)

- Once the actions are implemented, how long until they are verified as effective?

- Where will the verification activities be recorded?

- What verification indicators will be used (reduced scrap rates, reduced nonconformances, reduced customer complaints, trained personnel, and so on)?

- Do the indicators provide evidence that the actions solved the problem and didn't create any new ones?

- Will the actions require ongoing monitoring? If so, what is the frequency of the monitoring?

- Who will the verification results be reported to? How? When?

In order to provide an objective evaluation, it is suggested that personnel independent of the implemented actions be the ones who review the actions for effectiveness. The independent person's role is to perform a check and balance at the end of the problem-solving process. However, there is nothing wrong with the person(s) who implemented the action being present when the actions are being reviewed. In fact, that is suggested, because that person should be able to clearly describe, as well as show, confirmation of effectiveness of the actions taken.

CLOSURE

Once all of the implemented actions of a problem have been verified, the problem is considered resolved. The closure dates should be recorded in the organization's chosen method of tracking. Recording this date is important, as it provides the evidence that the problem is now resolved and all steps have been completed. Without completing the verification step, actions will appear in a perpetual state of "openness" and their status difficult to determine. Conversely, some organizations bypass the verification step altogether and close actions without verifying them. Unfortunately, without this step they will never be sure that the solution fixed the problem so it doesn't come back.

MONITORING

Long-term monitoring of implemented actions ensures that the solutions are working the way they were intended. It also determines whether or not the actions taken were the best long-term solution so that the problem will not occur again. Examples of monitoring may include SPC charts, internal audits, and check sheets that can track the performance of the activity over time. Again, a plan should be established to include long-term monitoring so that responsible personnel will ensure that monitoring happens and that the results are communicated and recorded as appropriate.

FINAL THOUGHT

The last step in the problem-solving process is to verify the implemented corrective and preventive actions for effectiveness. This verification step is vital in determining whether or not the action taken prevented the problem from recurring. When organizations fail to take this step, they are opening the door for repeat problems. The verifications need not be elaborate and may require that only a few questions be asked or performance observed by an independent party to determine effectiveness. The team will need to plan the verification methods to be used. They will also need to determine if long-term monitoring should be conducted, and if so, plan accordingly. The most important part of the verification step is that the results are recorded and reviewed by management personnel. If the corrective and preventive actions are not effective in preventing recurrence, then the team will need to revisit the root cause and the solutions that were selected.

REVIEW

Step 5
Verify and Monitor the Solutions

1. Plan how the corrective and preventive actions will be verified before implementation. Decide on:

   a. Methods to be used.

   b. Who will verify? If needed, who will monitor in the long term?

   c. How frequently will the monitoring activities occur?

   d. How long will the monitoring activities be in effect?

2. Use verification methods such as audits, tracking methods, and so on.

3. Verify actions as specified in the verification plan.

4. Close actions if they are working as planned.

5. Record results of the verification and ensure management personnel review them.

6. If actions are not effective, go back to root cause and solutions to reinvestigate.

Skill Builder

Review some past corrective and preventive actions that were implemented in your organization. How many of the actions were verified? What was the verification plan? Who was involved? What were the methods used? What were the results? In your opinion, were the actions taken effective?

8

Basic Problem-Solving Tools

This chapter focuses on some of the very basic, effective tools that teams can use. Even though some organizations use advanced tools, there are many organizations still learning how to apply the basics. While there are other detailed methods, books, and courses that teach problem-solving techniques, this chapter has been included to help the team get started in the right direction with examples of basic problem-solving tools.

SELECTING THE RIGHT TOOL

Many problem-solving processes have become overly reliant on picking the right tool. In the 1980s during the height of TQM, many organizations trained large numbers of people on problem-solving tools that resulted in little or no organizational improvement. The reason for this occurrence was that a formal methodology for carrying out problem solving was lacking or poorly implemented. Juran warned top management that taking a tool-oriented approach instead of a results-oriented approach was ineffective and that the use of statistical tools must not become an end in itself.[1]

Tools provide a way to tackle a problem. However, certain tools work better in different situations. At the foundation of many problem-solving processes is the fundamental tool of brainstorming. Even though brain-storming is a simple concept, it is often improperly executed, leaving teams exhausted and without the quantity of ideas they hoped to generate. Therefore, it is important that the necessary steps for using a particular tool are followed.

Tools can be categorized in two ways. When trying to generate many possibilities or ideas in order to investigate causes, use idea-generating tools such as:

- Brainstorming
- Brain writing
- Cause-and-effect diagram
- 5 Whys
- Affinity diagram

When more data is needed or the team is in the stage of analyzing facts, then the use of data gathering or analysis tools is more appropriate. Data gathering or analysis tools include:

- Check sheets
- Pareto diagrams
- Run charts
- Interviews
- Process mapping

PROBLEM-SOLVING TOOLS

Brainstorming

Purpose:

- To increase the team's ability to generate ideas
- To ensure nothing is overlooked

When to use:

- When it's important to go beyond the obvious
- When it's important to ensure that all details are discussed

Rules of brainstorming:

- No criticism is allowed—all ideas are good ideas.

- Each person has equal opportunity to express ideas.
- Quantity is more important than quality.
- Encourage piggybacking of ideas.

How to facilitate:

- Select a facilitator and a recorder (these may be the same person).
- Generate ideas one at a time, round-robin; if team members do not have ideas, it's OK to pass.
- Record ideas on flipchart paper for all to see—this helps for others to piggyback.

Brain Writing

Purpose:

- Brainstorming ideas by writing the ideas down and then sharing the ideas

When to use:

- When issues may be too difficult or emotional for members to verbally exchange ideas
- When avoiding "group think"
- When sessions are dominated by a few members

Rules:

- Follow the rules for brainstorming.

How to facilitate:

1. Facilitator writes a question or problem on flipchart.
2. Participants write as many ideas as possible using Post-It notes (one idea per note).
3. When participants have run out of ideas, Post-Its are put on wall.
4. Participants place the Post-Its into categories.
5. Participants may add more ideas—go back to step two.

5 Whys

Purpose:

- To help to identify the root causes of a problem and the relationship between causes

When to use:

- When team needs to look for root cause

- When the contributing causes are confusing

- When a visual tool is needed to explain the causes to others

How to facilitate:
(Use Post-Its, flipchart paper, pen)

1. Write problem on Post-It—place it at the far left of the paper.

2. Ask the group, "Why do we have this problem?" Write all ideas on Post-Its and place in row next to problem. Again ask, "Why does this situation create a problem?" Create another row of causes. Show relationships with arrows.

3. Continue to ask why (at least five times) about each cause until a fundamental answer appears, such as procedures, system, training needs, policies, and so on.

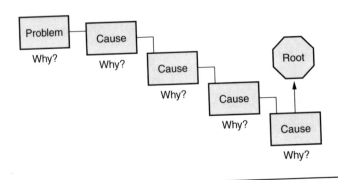

Figure 8.1   5 Whys.

Cause-and-Effect Diagram

Purpose:

- To identify possible causes of a specified problem
- To organize large amounts of information about a problem

When to use:

- When root cause needs to be identified
- When opinions or ideas about the problem are preventing the discovery of the root cause

How to design:

1. Agree on the problem statement (place in box on right).

2. Label each major category through brainstorming or use headings such as people, materials, equipment, work environment, methods.

3. Brainstorm all possible causes. Do not discuss solutions. After each suggestion ask, "Why does this happen?" in order to develop subcauses.

4. Analyze diagram and narrow the selection to determine a root cause.

5. Determine if cause selected may need more data gathering.

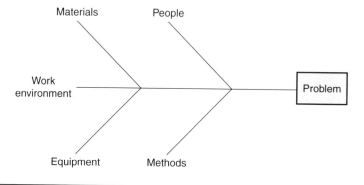

Figure 8.2　Cause-and-effect diagram.

Check Sheet

Purpose:

- For collecting data in a consistent format
- Used to collect baseline data
- Often used with other tools, such as Pareto diagrams, run charts, and so on

When to use:

- Collecting data to determine frequency, patterns, defects by type, defect location

How to design:

- Decide what is to be observed.
- Decide when data will be collected and for how long.
- Design form to fit need.

Work Order Errors				Week ending: 1/31/08		
Department: Manufacturing				Name: Bob Gem		
Error	1/27	1/28	1/29	1/30	1/31	Total
Missing information	JHT		JHT III	III	IIII	20
Changed information	IIII	IIII	JHT II	IIII	JHT III	27
Wrong information	I	I		I		3
Other:						
Total	10	5	15	8	12	50

Figure 8.3   Check sheet.

Pareto Diagram

Purpose:

- Ranks data by categories
- Helps team to direct its efforts to the few largest categories

When to use:

- When trying to focus on the most significant problem or cause

How to design:

1. Decide what categories you will use to group items.

2. Specify the time frame when the data will be collected.

3. Collect the data.

4. Determine scales for chart.

5. Construct and label bars for each category—start with largest to smallest category.

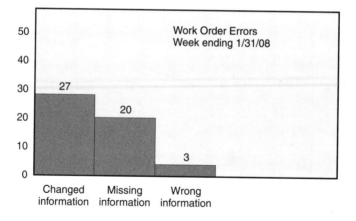

Figure 8.4   Pareto diagram.

Run Chart

Purpose:

- To review the system's behavior over time
- To distinguish trends
- To establish baseline data

When to use:

- A useful tool when showing the evolution of a situation over time

How to design:

1. Draw vertical axis based on number you expect to see.
2. Draw horizontal axis based on frequency (time).
3. Plot each measurement in the time order it occurs.
4. Connect points with straight lines.
5. Look for trends (7 points in one direction).

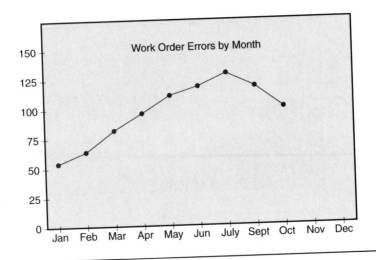

Figure 8.5   Run chart.

FINAL THOUGHT

Effective problem solving typically requires a combination of tools. No one tool is right in every situation. Picking the right tool for the problem will come through the experience of personnel using the tools. For each tool, this chapter explained its purpose, when to use it, and how to facilitate or design it. Because every organization is at different levels in their problem-solving approach, they should consider the information and training that is needed to ensure effective problem solving.

9

Importance of Effective Teams in the Problem-Solving Process

WHY DO WE NEED TEAMS?

Most organizations value the importance of teams. However, when selecting teams for problem-solving activities, some of the basics are forgotten. People are thrown into a room and expected to successfully resolve a problem in an hour, complete with a root cause and a solution. In the worst-case scenarios, one person tries to handle the issue without any support. While one individual may be able to make a difference in the organization, seldom does one person have the expertise and knowledge needed to understand everything that goes on in the organization. Very often, problem solving requires a cross-section of expertise. When a well-selected team pools its knowledge and skills, it often comes up with better ideas, innovations, and solutions than with just one person trying to go it alone.

Many successful organizations conduct team training to ensure that their problem-solving teams are given enough basic skills to get the job done. Therefore, when a team is called upon, many of the basics that will be discussed in this chapter have already been covered and the team simply goes to work. While many books and courses have been written about team development, this chapter is meant to provide an overview of the key elements of developing a team that may prove beneficial to those organizations desiring a more formal approach.

SELECTING THE TEAM

Selecting the right team members is important for problem-solving activities. If the members don't get along, don't have enough expertise, aren't owners of the process where the problem exists, or are not trained on the basics of problem solving, the team will struggle and may not achieve the results they need. A story that comes to mind in the selection of team members has to do with a colleague who was asked to figure out why a particular team was not successful. Upon investigation, she found that all the team members were detailed doers, but no one was a leader who could focus on the big picture. The team was so stuck in the nitty-gritty details that they were unable to move forward. She also found that the members of the team were downstream from the process where the problem existed, creating an atmosphere of trying to solve a problem that the members didn't fully understand or have expertise in.

When selecting a problem-solving team, the team should have the following characteristics:

- Process owner or knowledge of the process where the problem exists

- Team leader who can effectively facilitate discussions, run meetings, and communicate roadblocks and resource needs to top management

- Mix of members who are both detail oriented and big-picture oriented

The size of the team will vary depending on the size of the organization and the complexity of the problem. It would be common for a small organization to have a two-person team and a larger organization to have a five- or six-person team. It is not advised to have a team larger than five or six as it becomes more difficult to coordinate schedules and manage team activities. The team can also expand and contract as the different steps in the problem-solving process evolve. For instance, more technical experts may be asked to join the team when brainstorming the root cause. Once the cause is defined, the team would contract to its original size. The core team's responsibility is to ensure that the problem-solving activity is completed.

DEVELOPMENT OF THE TEAM

Many times people are asked to be part of a team. However, sometimes little thought is given to how much time the group may need to become an effective team. In order for a group to become a team, it will go through various stages of development. These stages are predictable; however, the amount of time spent in each stage can vary depending on how well the members know each other or the experience they have had in the past. While the team usually will go through these stages subconsciously, team leaders and team members who are aware of these stages usually are able to work through the different dynamics of team formation more smoothly. The various stages teams typically transition through were developed by Bruce W. Tuckman, who identified these five stages[1]:

1. Forming

2. Storming

3. Norming

4. Performing

5. Adjourning[2]

Forming

When the team is forming, they are testing the boundaries of the group. They may or may not fully participate and some may wonder why they were asked to join the team. The team will be more concerned at this point about how well they get along. At this stage, expect some members to discuss personal issues and complain about the organization or why the problem may be difficult to solve. To make the forming stage move smoothly, the team leader will need to ensure that:

• The members understand what the purpose of the team is, and are clear about the problem they will be working on.

• The team's expertise is acknowledged by each member stating why they were selected for the team.

• Methods are discussed for proceeding, that is, gathering information, frequency of meeting, roles of the members, and so on. The investigation action plan checklist (Figure 4.2, page 25) may be helpful in breaking the ice for the first meeting.

Unless the team has worked together in the past, the first meeting should be scheduled to allow the members to get acquainted. Don't make the first meeting the brainstorming session for determining root cause, since the team may not be forthcoming with ideas if they are trying to form. Once the team members feel comfortable with each other, they will be able to better accept challenges to their ideas or suggestions.

Storming

The storming stage is the most difficult of all the stages. At this point, some of the team members may not be cooperative and try to rely on their own experiences without collaborating with the rest of the team. They may be ruled by emotion rather than logic, thus causing the progress of the team to slow down. Some members may become frustrated or impatient with the lack of progress, and some may be habitually late for meetings or not show up at all! Also, the problem they have been asked to work on may appear different or more difficult than they first thought, causing them to place blame or become obstinate or uncooperative. In order to overcome the storming stage, the team leader will need to ensure that:

- The members are asked to share information and expertise relevant to the problem, and reinforce the value they are bringing to the table.

- Disagreements are managed so that the issues are explored.

- Steps aren't skipped in the problem-solving process or cut short during the investigation because of disagreements.

- The tendency of team members to compete or place blame is minimized.

- Members are allowed to work through the conflicts.

Once the team members feel they are important to the group and have valuable contributions to make, the storming stage will diminish. The team will become more cooperative and less competitive. Keep in mind that conflicts are valuable as they allow the team to explore many possibilities. However, conflicts must be managed so that the end result is constructive rather than destructive for the team.

Norming

During this stage, the opinions of the team are shared and emotional conflicts are resolved. The team becomes cohesive and progress moves forward. The team accepts the task at hand and becomes supportive to one another. Also at this stage, the team will be ready to be innovative and creative in solving the problem. The team leader can ensure their success at this stage by:

- Encouraging involvement of all members

- Acknowledging the team's contributions

- Keeping discussions on track and assigning action items
- Transferring the leadership role to various members as they work through their assignments
- Reconciling any differences between members

The team will be able to recognize that they are now working as a team, and a high level of trust and cohesiveness will be evident. They will approach the task at hand cooperatively and be able to share ideas, as well as offer constructive criticism.

Performing

Once the team has developed trust with one another, they will be able to settle into the task at hand. At this stage, they will be more creative and the challenge of solving the problem will seem easier. The team will be aware of their strengths and weaknesses. Once this happens, they will demonstrate genuine concern about the success of the problem-solving activity by carrying out their assignments and supporting each other in the achievement of the team's goal. The team leader can facilitate this stage by ensuring that mutual trust and acceptance is maintained, and that the team members help each other. The team is encouraged to be resourceful and flexible in its ideas. At this point, team members have developed a cohesiveness that will allow them to promote their cause outside of the team. They can now build alliances with others in the organization to ensure that the implementation step of the problem-solving process is successful.

These stages may be achieved in a relatively short period of time, depending on the team members. A skilled team leader can help to expedite the process and should be selected carefully. In some situations, the customer is at stake, and therefore it is important that problem-solving activities are carried out efficiently and effectively. In fact, in some industries, problem-solving teams must quickly determine a plan of action to deal with reported customer problems. Teams will not have weeks and weeks to determine root cause and solutions. Instead, they will be required to determine the actions within a matter of days.

Adjourning

The team has now completed their mission and there is no real reason for the team to continue. The team will want to ensure that the records and minutes of their activities are properly preserved. They may also want to include the cost savings that were realized through the success of their problem-solving efforts. This information should also be shared with management so they become aware of the successes that have been achieved and recognize that much has been gained by supporting the team and allocating resources for problem-solving activities. This type of communication will provide closure to the activity and also serve as recognition for the team.

ROLES OF THE TEAM

Teams are typically comprised of a leader, process owners, and a recorder. If a team is made up of two people, the team member or leader can also be the recorder. Establishing the roles of the members is important so that each understands what their purpose will be on the team. The following describes the responsibilities of each.

Team Leader

The team leader's purpose is to keep the discussion moving according to the agenda and ensure assignments are recorded and carried out. The team leader is the "go-to" person for the team and will need to be comfortable with presenting plans to management, asking for assistance to remove roadblocks, and/or asking for resources. Team leaders should possess the following skills:

- Project management skills
- Facilitation skills
- Ability to resolve conflicts
- Ability to communicate with people at all levels in the organization
- Knowledge of the organization's problem-solving process and problem-solving tools
- Listening skills
- Ability to ask questions to get the team started, draw people out, build the team
- Become a resource for the team
- Organizational skills to ensure that meetings are structured and records are kept

Team Members

Process owners usually make up the membership on a team. Process owners are those individuals that are either responsible for or have demonstrated knowledge of the process where the problem has occurred. They are invaluable to the team, as they have the expertise to determine root cause and determine feasible solutions. However, those closest to the process may sometimes be more focused on the emotions of the issue rather than fact. The team leader will want to ensure that the team's recommendations have been based on a reasonable amount of homework. The team members should be capable of the following:

- Problem-solving skills and knowledge of the necessary tools. (It is acceptable to add new members to the team that aren't as skilled in problem solving. If this is the case, the team leader and/or other members should act as coaches to the new members.)

- Take responsibility for assignments.

- Ability and desire to work in a team setting.

- Expertise and knowledge of the process being affected by the problem.

- Be receptive to change.

- Be receptive to ideas from other team members.

Recorder

Taking good notes of the meetings and actions is important and helps to build a history of the problems the organization has resolved. If the team is larger, a person recording the minutes other than the team leader will be needed. The reason is that facilitating a larger team takes special skills. It is often difficult to do an adequate job of functioning as the leader while taking concise and complete notes. This role can be rotated among the team members or be designated to someone else from the organization that has the skills for being a scribe. This person may also assist the team leader in recording brainstorming activities on flipcharts as the meetings are facilitated. The recorder should have the following skills:

- Good listening and writing skills in order to capture brief minutes, action items, and major decisions

- Word processing skills or other computer skills to handle the information during or after the meeting

- Responsibility to distribute minutes to the team

Creating a template that outlines the steps used in the problem-solving activity can save time in creating minutes. It will also keep the format consistent, making it easier to compare notes for current activities and historical purposes.

CONDUCTING EFFECTIVE MEETINGS

Many organizations train their personnel on conducting meetings. However, ask yourself the last time people knew the reason for the meeting, showed up on time, or were concerned about the results of the meeting. Besides problem-solving meetings, most organizations conduct many meetings, including management reviews, departmental meetings, staff meetings, financial reviews, and so on. Meetings that are conducted ineffectively waste time and money.

In order to ensure meetings are effective and efficient, a structured approach should be used. While the RMR structure listed below doesn't guarantee perfect results, it is a tool that can be used to ensure that the basic meeting fundamentals are present and the lack of them doesn't ambush a well-intended meeting. When a meeting is called, the *reasons, methods,* and *results* (RMR) should be communicated.

Reasons:

- Why are we here?

- Why have I been selected to attend—what can I offer?

- What is our goal?

Methods:

- What is the agenda?

- How frequently will we meet and for how long?

- What project or activity will we be working on?

- What are the steps we will be following?

- What are my responsibilities?

- What is expected from me?

- What is expected from the team?

Results:

- Who will benefit from this?
- When do we need to be finished?
- How will we know when we have achieved our goal? What is our output?

Meetings should begin by summarizing or reviewing what took place at the last meeting. The team leader or recorder can do this. This review will provide an equal starting point for all members. Next, review any assignments or action items so that the team knows where they stand in conjunction with their project. At the end of the meeting, the team leader should summarize the team's progress in relation to the established goal. Finally, the date and time of the next meeting should be announced. As mentioned earlier, there are cases where this approach will not be feasible if the team only has several days to come up with the answers.

Conducting meetings is a process in itself. Some organizations are trying to improve the way in which they conduct meetings and to evaluate whether or not their meetings are effective. At the end of a meeting, some organizations complete an evaluation such as the one shown in Figure 9.1.

Criteria	Rank 1–5 (5 being excellent)
Reason clearly stated and agenda available	
Meeting started on time	
Meeting summary of last meeting was presented	
Participants came prepared	
Participants contributed actively	
Discussion dealt with the issue and didn't deviate to personal agendas	
Members supported the team leader	
Viewpoints were accepted without put-downs	
Previous action items were presented and updated	
New action items were assigned	
Team's progress was summarized	
Next meeting date and time was communicated	
Meeting ended on time	

Figure 9.1   Evaluation at the end of a meeting.

FINAL THOUGHT

With the amount of meetings conducted every day in organizations, the time spent needs to be well worth it, not only for those involved in the meetings, but also for the organization. Meetings take time, and time equates into resources. Consequently, poorly conducted meetings should not become the problem. Without formal approaches for selecting the teams and for conducting the meetings, more may be lost than gained. Well-trained teams, along with efficient, effective meetings, will enhance rather than detract from the importance of sharing ideas, knowledge, and expertise.

Skill Builder

Evaluate your own meetings. Do people show up on time? Is the purpose well stated? Are team members aware of their roles? In your opinion, could your meetings be more effective? How? What would you change?

10

The Road to Continual Improvement

Quality comes not from inspection but from improvement of the process.

—W. Edwards Deming

MAKING THE DECISION TO IMPROVE

What is improvement? Many organizations believe that if they fix a certain issue or resolve a specific customer complaint or product issue, they have improved the overall performance of the organization. While these actions may lead to some improvement, the long-range effect may not address the inefficiencies found throughout the organization. When solving a problem, the concept of improvement must extend beyond just the immediate problem. In fact, the likelihood is that the same problem could potentially exist in other areas of the organization.

Webster defines improvement as "an addition or change that improves something; to raise to a better quality or condition." Tack on the word "continual" and the intensity of this activity increases. This means that in order to achieve continual improvement, *an addition or change that improves something* must happen over and over again, recurring repeatedly over a long period of time. There is no doubt that every organization wants to improve. However, for continual improvement to become a reality, improvement activities must be ongoing and not be interrupted by the next fad.

There are two types of improvement efforts found in many organizations. The first type is *incremental improvements*. These are small in scope, and may or may not take an abundance of resources or require full organizational involvement. These improvements are small steps typically taken over time, and improvements of this type are usually discussed in terms of pieces of a process. Juran believed that quality improvement, even though it has associated costs, should not be capital-intensive. He maintained that fine-tuning processes achieved the great majority of published improvements. He also believed that if a process was already producing 80 percent good work, then the fine-tuning could bring the performance of the process into the high 90s without capital investment.[1]

The second type is *breakthrough improvements.* These improvements are larger in scope, usually involve cross-functional commitment and resources, and may lead to redesigning old processes or designing and implementing new ones. Examples of breakthrough improvements might include revamping a manual order entry or scheduling process to an electronic system, analyzing the profitability of customers and narrowing the customer base by eliminating those that are not profitable, or expanding products or services by changing technologies or equipment. Breakthrough projects of this type can significantly alter the way work is done and may require the approval of capital expenditures for possible equipment modifications, as well as additional training to raise competency levels in order to handle the changes.

Management will need to select improvement projects carefully, since no organization has an unlimited supply of time, money, or people. When choosing improvement projects, the question that should be asked is: If we improve this aspect of what we do, how will we better serve our customers? How will this improvement move us closer to achieving our objectives?

DEVELOPING A CONTINUAL IMPROVEMENT PHILOSOPHY

Before an organization can develop a continual improvement process, they must first develop a continual improvement philosophy. That is, management must consider how they support improvement activities and what message they send to the workforce. In order to foster a philosophy of continual improvement, the following concepts should be considered:

- Creating a culture so that people actively seek improvement opportunities

- Delegating authority so that people are empowered and accept responsibility for improvement actions

- Developing and communicating business objectives so that people are clear on what is important to the organization
- Understanding the cost of poor quality
- Thinking "outside the box" by looking at other industries and benchmarking
- Stressing efficiency and effectiveness of processes
- Rewarding achievement and innovation
- Rewarding prevention rather than firefighting

Besides developing the philosophies listed above, organizations should develop a process for improving. Improvements don't happen by accident; instead, they are planned events that are managed. Before management launches the organization in multiple directions with multiple improvement projects, they should determine the reason for improvement.

Management should also be in agreement that the improvement is needed and be willing to commit resources. Without this commitment, the project may be put on hold or cancelled midstream, therefore sending the message that improvement isn't important. To begin the process of determining if improvement is needed, the following questions should be asked:

1. What is the purpose of the improvement project?

2. What is the size and scope of this project? Does it affect the whole company or certain parts of it?

3. What types of resources are needed?

4. What is the current performance of this process? In other words, what kind of information do we currently have that is measuring the output of the process? What are the inputs to the process?

5. Are we able to tell if the process being considered for improvement is stable or in a state of crisis? If it is in a state of crisis, what will it take to stabilize it so we can move forward to improve?

Keep in mind that different types of improvements will require various levels of support. It is important also to consider other activities that are going on in the organization to prevent resource overload. Examples of activities in the organization that can put a strain on resources include things like implementing an ERP system, workforce reduction, expanding or moving locations, and so on.

PRIORITIZING IMPROVEMENT ACTIVITIES

Many organizations make the mistake of trying to do too many improvement projects at once. This results in depleting resources, exhausting personnel, and carrying out projects with less than desirable outcomes. Organizations must prioritize the improvement activities. This prioritization should be driven by the goals the organization has already set. If the organization has identified many projects, applying the cost of quality is one way to help determine which projects will yield the biggest gains. If the organization hasn't been in the practice of formally implementing a lot of improvements, it may want to select a project that will show success in a short period of time in order to boost morale and get personnel excited about participating in future improvement activities.

QUICK FORMULA FOR THE COST OF QUALITY

The *cost of quality* is a quick estimate of the typical costs usually associated with poor quality. However, Philip Crosby coined two terms: the price of conformance (POC) and price of nonconformance (PONC).[2] *Price of conformance* is money invested in developing processes or systems, doing activities, or extra efforts that prevent nonconformances. Examples of the price of conformance would include training, setting up an ISO 9001:2008 quality management system, preventive maintenance, establishing a calibration system, order entry reviews, and so on. The *price of nonconformance* are the costs associated with things that go wrong, such as reprocessing, returns, reruns, downtime, and so on.

Crosby also identified a third part of the equation that must be considered. These are the costs associated with running the business provided that no costs are incurred due to nonconformances, rework, or waste. This means that the system is operating as it was intended and includes expenses such as materials, labor, energy, or equipment. When organizations are monitoring their expenses, they need to consider all three types. If management only looks at business expenses, they will miss the opportunity to eliminate costs associated with poor quality. If they look upon the price of conformance costs as a regular business expense, they may inadvertently eliminate processes or activities that are helping them to achieve good quality. When price of conformance is only looked upon as a business expense, it is not uncommon to see things like training, quality initiatives, even the frequency of preventive maintenance reduced or eliminated when budgets need to be cut. Unfortunately, management doesn't always perceive these activities as preventing poor quality from happening, but as non-value-added expenses to the organization.

Most organizations realize that bad quality has a cost. However, most never really calculate the vastness of its price to the organization. Calculating the cost of nonconformances is useful when trying to determine how big a problem really is and whether or not it warrants improvement. Many times, organizations ignore certain problems because they appear to be insignificant. However, when the effort is made to calculate the costs of nonconformances into real dollars, management is often surprised at how much is being wasted.

In order to make this estimate, some information will have to be gathered, such as estimated wages and unit selling price of the product or service. However, it needs to be emphasized that the final number is only a ballpark figure. Also, it is important to calculate the estimate over time. For instance, how much will this cost the organization if the problem continues for six months or one year?

Because this calculation is an estimate, it is conceivable that the real cost could be slightly higher or slightly lower. The idea is to bring the issue to management's attention and use these costs as a way to assist in prioritizing improvement projects. The following example demonstrates how to figure the cost of nonconformances.

The 100-Part Mistake

Many organizations make production errors every day and therefore scrap parts. When working with a job that produces hundreds or thousands of parts, 100 bad parts can go unnoticed. In fact, the people producing the product may see these types of problems occurring every day, but because the error seems small, nothing is done. When figuring the cost of nonconformances for this example, the calculations shown in Figure 10.1 need to be considered.

While this is only a 100-part problem, it represents a chunk of change. If this symbolizes only one problem, how many other problems may exist in this organization and how big could the losses be? Calculating the cost of nonconformances can play a major role in helping to determine where improvements should be made. Also, costs are relative. In one organization, $164,160.00 may represent an out of control situation. In others, this may only represent a small issue. The point to emphasize is that costs are real and therefore need to be considered so that improvement efforts are focused in a direction that can really help the organization.

Calculation	Cost
Wages of those who were involved in producing the product *Example:* 4 operators produced the product. Two hours of labor each, average wage $25.00 per hour. *Calculation:* 4 operators × 2 hours = 8 hours of labor × $25.00	$ 200.00
Wages of those who were involved in trying to solve the problem *Example:* Operations manager, two operators, quality manager: Two hours each. *Calculation:* Wage: $60 + $50 + $50 = $160.00 wages × 2 hours	$ 320.00
Unit selling price of product *Example:* *Calculation:* $10.00 per part × 100 parts	$ 1000.00
Monthly Cost Add wages plus unit price $520 + $1000.00 Multiply times the number for frequency of occurrence in the past month *Example:* 9 × $1520.00	$ 1520.00
Subtotal	$ 13,680.00
To estimate how big this problem may become if left unchecked: *Example:* $13,680.00 × 12 months	$164,160.00

Figure 10.1   Calculations for the cost of nonconformances.

USING DATA FROM THE ORGANIZATION TO DRIVE IMPROVEMENT

Part of managing the improvement process is to ensure that the data available within the organization is used effectively. Most organizations understand the concept but are not sure what data to collect or what to do with it once it is collected. Typically, organizations collect mounds and mounds of data. However, many times a good portion of the data never gets turned into something useful. Also, some people think that the pure act of collecting and crunching a lot of numbers will help them improve. The key to collecting critical information in order to identify improvement opportunities is to know where to look, what is important, and what to do with it.

Often, management teams will sit in a room and "present" information to one another. That is, each person will present the current numbers one at a time for their area, and then sit down. The problem with this approach is that the management team is presenting information, but not "sharing and using" it. Think about it. How much more effective would these meetings be if the management team spent their time in reviewing and analyzing information that was summarized in a format from which they could make educated decisions that were based on facts? Ultimately, these decisions would evolve into actions for improvement. When sharing information, management should insure that the data is compiled and presented in an easy-to-understand format such as run charts, Pareto charts, reports, and so on. Conversely, reviewing just raw data is not efficient in management meetings.

COLLECTING AND ANALYZING INFORMATION FOR IMPROVEMENT ACTIVITIES

The following sources are examples of where to gather information for continual improvement activities. Many of these were identified earlier as inputs for determining corrective and preventive actions. The list below includes many of the requirements for ANSI/ISO/ASQ Q9001:2008. However, all information should be considered in regard to management review and analysis of data.

- Customer feedback (that is, complaints, surveys, customer visits)

- Product conformity and performance data (that is, nonconformances, yields, scrap)

- Audit results (internal, external)

- Process measurements

- Corrective and preventive actions

- Customer returns

- Warranty issues

- Supplier problems

- Trended information

- Risk analysis

- Market analysis

- Employee surveys

- Service delivery data

- Self-assessment data

- Test data

- Financial data

With all of the sources listed above, where does an organization begin? First, the organization must look at what data is currently being collected in the areas important to them. Take an inventory of all the charts and graphs that are collected daily, monthly, quarterly, and so on. Who collects them? How often? Why? Information should also include comparison. For instance, rather than only looking at this quarter's results, look at how the results compare to last quarter's or last year's. Are the results positive or negative in regard to reaching the goals or objectives?

Remember, every picture tells a story. For each and every one of these pictures, ask the two fundamental questions, "Does it tell us anything that will help us run our business better?" "Do the measures assist us in making decisions that will help us to achieve our objectives and better satisfy the customer?" It is a waste of time to collect data for the sake of collecting data, not to mention the time wasted in creating charts that do not provide any value to the organization.

ESTABLISHING GOALS FOR IMPROVEMENT

When establishing goals for improvement, data becomes essential in determining the organization's current status. Sometimes management sets goals that may not be achievable based on their current performance. For instance, data gathered for determining an increase in sales should happen before the goal is established, to define the "as is" in order to make an assessment about "what could be." Once the feasibility of the goal is understood, the metrics can be developed in order to monitor the improvement.

Therefore, if we are looking at achieving a 15 percent increase in sales this year, questions that should be asked include:

- What type of skills does our sales force have?

- Do they have adequate knowledge about the products and services they are selling or do they promise the moon to the customer only to find out it can't be done, causing them to try to do it anyway at the expense of the organization?

- Do we reward this type of behavior?

- What kinds of marketing activities have been initiated?

- What is known about market trends?

- Is the 15 percent increase realistic for the particular product or service the organization is promoting?

- How does the customer perceive the organization's products in comparison to the competitor's?

- What is the market share and is it continuing to rise?

- Is the increase based on working harder and hoping for a return?

IMPLEMENTING CONTINUAL IMPROVEMENT

Once continual improvement goals and measurements for those goals are developed and formalized, management must communicate them within the organization to ensure that everyone understands their role and how they can help the organization achieve the improvements.

Once the information has been communicated, the next step is putting it into action. The organization should develop a standardized format to track the improvement activities. This is useful to show progress along the way and to ensure that the continual improvement goals are being met. Management should hold periodic meetings to review the status of these goals to ensure that any roadblocks are eliminated as they occur. Furthermore, if the goals are not being met, management will need to investigate why and take action to get the improvement activities back on track.

Some organizations make the mistake of trying to establish improvement projects midstream without taking into consideration the objectives of the organization. If improvement projects aren't tied to the overall achievement of the objectives, then resources may be wasted on projects that will not improve the condition of the business. For instance, some organizations set their people free to come up with ideas on ways to improve the organization. These projects are selected as random events without guidance and personnel are asked to report on their successes. While there may be a lot of applauding and back-slapping over their accomplishments, there may be no real benefit to the organization in terms of improving the overall operation because the improvements are not connected to the organizational objectives.

Another problem organizations face is attempting to go after the "big improvements" that have high visibility, such as revamping an entire system. These types of improvements are resource-intensive and, unless they have been thoughtfully analyzed and implemented, may cause more internal frustration and customer loss than gain. An example is of one organization that decided to improve its order fulfillment process by revamping the entire system from order entry to delivery of their product. When the new process was turned on, customer orders were not delivered according to the scheduled delivery dates, orders were incorrectly shipped, and customer complaints were being received in droves by every position in the organization. Employees who previously prided themselves on how well they had satisfied the customers were now on the verge of quitting, because the stress and frustration levels could not be tolerated. What did this cost the organization? How could they have prevented such a fiasco? Quite obviously, their improvement plan was not complete and the right questions were not asked by management.

TYING IT ALL TOGETHER

The 10 steps listed below describe a generic continual improvement process, which includes references to the ANSI/ISO/ASQ Q9001:2008 requirements. Any size or type of organization can use this to get started. This example gives an organization a basic approach for identifying improvement opportunities and can be modified to fit the organization's business management system.

1. *Identify key performance metrics.* The organization should identify the key performance metrics to be monitored. These metrics would be based on business objectives, customer requirements, suppliers, manufacturing, quality, and so on. *(5.4.1 Quality objectives; 8.1 General; 8.2.1 Customer satisfaction; 8.2.3 Monitoring and measurement of processes; 8.2.4 Monitoring and measurement of product)*

2. *Establish methods for collecting and reporting data.* For each of these metrics, methods of collecting and reporting this information should be established. It is advantageous to put the data in charts and/or reports to effectively communicate the results. This approach allows management to more easily analyze the data. Typically, reporting this data should occur monthly and/or quarterly. *(8.1 General)*

3. *Analyze data.* These metrics are analyzed in management meetings (that is, management review or similar). The inputs to management review in ANSI/ISO/ASQ Q9001:2008 provide many opportunities to analyze and discuss the data from the management system. These discussions should lead to determining areas for improvement. *(5.6 Management review; 8.4 Analysis of data)*

4. *Determine areas for improvement based on results of data.* Management should determine the areas that need improvement based on the analysis of data. This analysis should provide management with the ability to develop improvement actions. *(5.6 Management review; 8.4 Analysis of data; 8.5.1 Continual improvement)*

5. *Develop and implement continual improvement actions.* Continual improvement actions should be developed and implemented per an action plan. Along with the actions, management should determine owners, resources, and due dates to ensure that the actions are completed. *(8.5.1 Continual improvement)*

6. *Verify actions to determine effectiveness.* After the actions have been implemented, verification activities should occur to ensure that the actions taken were effective. *(8.5.2 Corrective Action; 8.5.3 Preventive Action)*

7. *Review results of verification.* The results of this verification should be reviewed by management and other appropriate personnel. *(5.6 Management review)*

8. *Determine if results are satisfactory.* Management decides if actions implemented were effective as planned. *(5.6 Management review)*

9. *If not, revisit action plan and modify.* If the improvement actions were not effective, management should revisit the action plan and modify it.

10. *If yes, communicate improvements to the organization.* Management should communicate the improvements to personnel in the organization. This communication enables personnel to understand the improvements that affect them as well as to ensure that they are aware of the effectiveness of the management system. *(5.5.3 Internal communication)*

Refer to appendix G, which describes how these 10 steps are integrated.

FINAL THOUGHT

Every day that a problem is left unsolved is a day where money is left on the table. In other words, problems stay problems and cost the business money until they are fixed permanently, never to return again. These are not profound thoughts, but simply reality for many organizations. Without a structured approach to solving problems and improving, the organization stays in a state of perpetual chaos. Consequently, over time, the organization will continue to decline in its customer service, product/service quality, and employee morale, until it eventually bites the dust.

Continual improvement in itself is a process that must be managed. It is not a process that can simply exist on its own. Furthermore, for the process to succeed, it must have top management's commitment to allocating the necessary resources, eliminating roadblocks, and promoting the concept of prevention throughout the organization. With these implemented effectively, the organization is well on its way to the never-ending road of continual improvement.

11

Case Study

The ACME Manufacturing company is a high-volume electro-mechanical component manufacturer. The product that ACME makes is sold mainly to the automotive industry. Since their automotive customers demand quick responses to problems, the ACME company has implemented a five-step problem-solving process. Every employee has been trained in this process. The company considers this process to be a vital key to its ongoing success with its customers.

The management team at ACME empowers employees to create ad hoc cross-functional problem-solving teams as needed. The managers insist that solving the customers' problems in a timely and effective manner will enable ACME to continue to grow and prosper in the future. Since instituting this process five years ago, ACME has seen a reduced number of customer complaints, a reduced number of internal rejects, and a reduced scrap rate.

Recently, the Babit Manufacturing company called to complain that the last shipment of ACME product was defective. When further questioned by the ACME customer service representative, the customer explained that the product was not working in the intended application. This isolated the problem as ACME's. Fortunately, only 10 defective products had been used, so the rest of the shipment was still packaged.

The ACME customer service representative immediately issued a return material authorization number to the customer to return the product. The ACME representative also requested that all ten of the defective components be sent back to ACME overnight for immediate testing by ACME engineers. The customer service representative then contacted the ACME operations manager to alert her of the suspect product. The operations manager then ensured that all finished goods of the same part number were put on hold. Fortunately, at that time there was no work-in-process. These actions just described were considered "fast fixes." Babit Manufacturing requested that no replacement product be sent until the root cause of the problem was found.

Upon receiving the returned product, the ACME engineers ran a series of tests to reproduce the failure and confirmed the customer's claim that the 10 units were defective. Upon discovering this, the engineers created an ad-hoc, cross-functional problem-solving team. The team included personnel from engineering, operations, quality, maintenance, and logistics. Because Babit's production line was shut down until the issue was resolved, the team met immediately to begin their five-step problem-solving process. This five-step process, along with the review sections, is described in the remainder of this case study. The team initiated a problem resolution report to document their process, which is found at the end of the case study (page 89).

STEP 1: DESCRIBE THE PROBLEM

The team reviewed the information from the ACME customer service representative and from the testing data, and then created the 4W/2H/1C table as shown in Table 11.1. From this table, the team was able to develop the problem description listed below. This statement gives enough details to get the team started in the problem-solving process.

Table 11.1   ACME's 4W/2H/1C table.

	Question	Answer
W	What was affected?	Babit Mfg. Part #842AC37
W	Where did the problem take place?	At the Louisville facility
W	When was the problem discovered?	On 6/25/08 @ 9:30 AM (first shift)
W	Who discovered the problem?	Babit Mfg.—Mary Jones— Line D operator
H	How much was affected?	400 units of ACME Part #MST4982
H	How often has this problem occurred?	First-time occurrence— no previous record
C	What is the consequence of this situation?	400 units shipped back to ACME; 200 units on hold in ACME finished goods inventory; No in-process units at ACME; Babit's Line D is shut down until issue is resolved.

A shipment of 400 components (#MST4982) was shipped to Babit Manufacturing on 6/18/08. The component would not work in the customer's product #842AC37. The defective product was found by the customer on their Line D. Ten tested samples of #MST4982 showed that the parameter G was out of specification by five milliseconds. The remainder of the Babit order (390 units) is being shipped back to ACME. This situation has delayed the manufacturing of Babit's product.

Review

By using the 4W/2H/1C formula, the team was able to narrow down the problem description in terms that everyone could understand. All of the necessary information pertaining to the problem was captured in their problem description. Describing the problem is the first step in the problem-solving process. Furthermore, a clear problem description will focus the team and will help eliminate any wasted time and energy by attempting to solve the wrong problem.

STEP 2: INVESTIGATE THE CAUSE

In order to expedite the process, the team created the checklist in Figure 11.1 to assist them in resolving the problem. After completing the checklist, the team generated a cause-and-effect diagram to identify possible causes. The diagram in Figure 11.2 is the first pass at identifying the possible causes of the problem. The team continued to brainstorm possible causes under each subheading.

Once the team had created a cause-and-effect diagram, the next step was to select the most likely cause(s) in order to determine the root cause. During this time, the team collected and analyzed data and evaluated the options. The team also used the "5 Whys" approach shown in Table 11.2 to determine the root cause.

With this information, the team was able to define the root cause as:

There is not a process for training temporary employees.

With the root cause of the problem found, the next step for the team was to determine the actions (solutions) that would address the root cause.

Investigation Action Plan Checklist		
Describe the fast fix that was taken: *Ten units of suspect product returned from Babit Manufacturing and tested by ACME engineers. Units in ACME finished goods inventory have been put on hold.*		
Is the fix working at the moment? (If not, explain what will be done in the short term.)	(Yes)	
	No	
List the owner of the problem: *Jeri Cain (Operations Manager)* List those who need to be involved: *Jack Russell (Team leader)* *Team members: K. Leach, S. Smith, R. Jones, G. Harding*		
List information currently available to assist in the investigation: Data: *Raw material, in-process, and final inspection data* *(for dates 6/1/08–6/15/08)* Employee input: *Need to question Line 5 operators (all shifts)* Flowcharts of the process: *none* Procedures: *SOP #MH004 Material Handling for Raw Materials, SOP #QA003 In-Process Inspection; SOP #QA005 Final Inspection* Records: *Manufacturing and final inspection records* *(for dates 6/1/08–6/15/08)*		
Has the problem occurred in the past? Yes / (No) If yes, what records exist?		
Frequency of Meetings: (daily, weekly, etc.) *Daily* Time: *2:00 p.m.* Place: *Conference room 4* First meeting date: *7/01/08*		

Figure 11.1   Investigation action plan checklist.

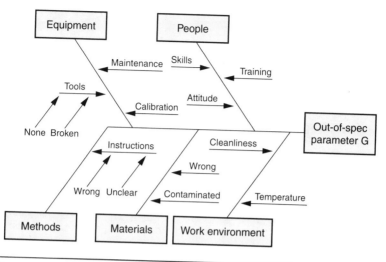

Figure 11.2 Cause-and-effect example.

Table 11.2 ACME's "5 Whys" table.

5 Whys	Answer
Why was the product defective?	Because parameter G was out of specification by 5 milliseconds.
Why was parameter G out of spec?	Because an incorrect chemical was added to the Line 5 process. *(Chemical #13567 instead of Chemical #88765)*
Why did an incorrect chemical get added to the Line 5 process?	Because the material handler did not know how to select the right chemical for the process.
Why did the material handler not know how to select the right chemical for the process?	Because the material handler had not received training.
Why did the material handler not receive training?	Because he was a temporary employee and there is not a process for training temporary employees.

Review

> The team used a combination of two problem-solving tools—the cause-and-effect diagram and the 5 Whys. The cause-and-effect diagram enabled the team to look at *all* possible causes, which is why it is a brainstorming activity. The 5 Whys focused the team to follow a sequence of questions that eventually led them to identifying the root cause. The challenge for teams in this situation is to utilize a combination of tools in order to successfully identify the root cause. Many teams simply give up too soon or quickly identify a symptom as a root cause. As you can see, the root cause might be different than the team may have originally thought.

STEP 3: SELECT AND TEST SOLUTIONS

At this step in the process, the team generated a set of potential solutions, collected and analyzed information about the most likely solution, and, finally, determined the best actions to take. They used brainstorming for this step. In order to make the session more useful, the team leader requested additional personnel to participate in this part of the process. It was important to get the right people in the room that would have the insight necessary to choose the best solutions. The brainstorming list they developed is found below.

Potential Solutions *(Corrective and Preventive Actions)*

- Develop training process for temporary material handlers *(corrective)*. This process will include:

  - Training of temporary material handlers and retraining of existing material handlers *(corrective)*

  - Developing training checklists for material handlers *(corrective)*

- Determine which activities temporary employees can be assigned to throughout the company *(preventive)*.

- Establish a companywide process for training temporary employees so they are not released to work areas before training *(preventive)*.

Once the team had exhausted all of the brainpower within their group, it was time to determine the solutions that were feasible to implement. They

Impact Analysis			
Root Cause: *Lack of training process for temporary employees*			
Proposed Solution: *Develop a training process for temporary employees*			
Analysis	How will the solution impact the system?	Positive ✓	Negative ✓
Cost	Minimal—will be required to pay temporary employees for the time they spend in training	✓	
Safety	None	–	–
Product	Will ensure product meets customer specifications	✓	
Process	Will ensure that the processes are followed correctly	✓	
Customer	Customer specifications will be met	✓	
Supplier	None	–	–

Figure 11.3   ACME's impact analysis.

proceeded to create an impact analysis for the proposed solutions. An example of one of those is shown in Figure 11.3.

Review

The team utilized the collective knowledge of its members to determine the actions that would ultimately prevent the problem from recurring. By creating the impact analysis, they were able to assess the impact of the solutions they developed. Many organizations determine action items based on what they wish they could have rather than a feasible solution. At this stage in the process, the team must ensure that they have representation from the appropriate individuals to assure that the proposed solutions are feasible.

STEP 4: IMPLEMENT THE SOLUTIONS

When assigning personnel to the actions, the team thought about the resources that were available in the organization and what roadblocks might pop up in the near future. When thinking about due dates, the teams were realistic with the length of time it would take to get the actions implemented, which included training the necessary personnel in new processes.

The list of action items they created to resolve the problem is shown in Figure 11.4.

As shown in Figure 11.4, the corrective actions implemented took care of the training issue with the material handlers. The training checklist would ensure temporary material handlers were adequately trained before they began their job. The preventive actions ensured that, throughout the company, temporary employees would not fall through the cracks and would receive necessary training. It was also determined that the company needed to assess which activities in the organization could be handled by temporary employees.

Corrective Action	Assigned To	Due Date
1. Develop a training process to ensure training of temporary material handlers.	L. Bell	7/10/08
2. Train temporary material handlers in SOP #MH004; retrain existing material handlers in SOP #MH004.	J. Jones	7/10/08
3. Create a training checklist for temporary material handlers.	K. Smith	7/15/08
Preventive Action		
1. Determine which activities temporary employees can be assigned to throughout the company.	M. Collins	7/15/08
2. Establish a companywide process for training temporary employees so they are not released to work areas before being trained.	T. Robinson	7/25/08

Figure 11.4 ACME's action items.

Once the corrective and preventive action plans were developed, they were handed off to the quality manager to monitor the implementation of the actions. Each assignee was responsible for keeping the quality manager informed of progress, including any roadblocks. After two months from completion of the actions, the quality manager selected an internal auditor to verify and close the actions.

Review

This is one of the critical steps in the problem-solving process. In other words, actions are what make the changes necessary in the organization, to prevent problems from recurring and potential problems from occurring. Many organizations miss the significance of this step. Instead, they put pressure on the problem-solving teams to "hurry up and fix it," rather than allowing the time necessary to put the correct actions in place. Furthermore, actions are just one piece of this step. The other steps include assigning the right personnel for each action and assigning due dates for completion. Without these two, actions won't happen. They will simply slip through the cracks and disappear until the problem creeps back into the organization and the process starts all over again!

STEP 5: VERIFY AND MONITOR THE SOLUTIONS

Approximately two months after the last action had been completed, an internal quality auditor verified that the actions taken had been implemented effectively. The auditor conducted the following verification activities:

For the Implemented Corrective Actions

- Reviewed the flowchart that described the training process for temporary material handlers.

- Reviewed the training records of all material handlers to ensure that they were trained in SOP #MH004.

- Reviewed a copy of the training checklist for temporary material handlers.

For the Implemented Preventive Actions

- Confirmed that a companywide list was developed that defines which activities temporary employees could do.

- Reviewed the flowchart that described the companywide training process for temporary employees.

- Observed performance of temporary employees performing the material handling tasks against the procedure to verify training effectiveness.

- Observed performance of temporary employees in other defined areas and verified performance according to procedures.

Once the internal quality auditor verified all the actions, the problem was officially "closed" in the problem resolution tracking database. Because ACME used a database to track these actions, the quality manager was able to quickly run reports to show which action items were open and which were closed. This enabled the quality manager to determine if escalation steps were needed in the event actions were not being taken as planned.

The last step in this process for ACME was to determine what, if any, actions were necessary to monitor the implemented actions. The quality manager decided to add the following items to the internal quality auditor weekly checklist to monitor the situation for the next three months:

1. Review a random sample of temporary employee training records.

2. Observe performance of temporary employees to their procedures.

Review

The verification activities are critical to the success of the problem-solving process. Without verifying the implemented actions, you won't know if they were effective in preventing the problem from recurring. In other words, what worked and what didn't? Many times, information gathered from actions that were not effective is just as valuable as from actions that were effective. Lessons are everywhere you look in an organization. World-class organizations applaud their employees for their effort in trying to solve problems and prevent new ones, regardless if they don't always get it right the first time.

Problem Resolution Report

Initiation Date: __7/1/2008__   PRR# __75__

Initiated By: __Jack Russell__

Problem Description:
A shipment of 400 components (#MST4982) was shipped to Babit Mfg. on 6/18/08. Component does not work in customer part #842AC47. Problem found on Babit Line D. Ten tested samples showed Parameter G out of spec by five milliseconds. Remainder of suspect product (390 units) is being shipped back. Problem has delayed Babit Manufacturing.

Interim Actions: (Fast Fix)	Assigned To	Due Date
1. Issue Babit Manufacturing RMA# to return suspect product	A. Hardy	6/25/2008
2. Request return of 10 samples for testing	A. Hardy	6/25/2008
3. Alert operations manager	A. Hardy	6/25/2008
4. Check ACME in-process and final goods inventory	W. Benson	6/25/2008

Root Cause:
There is not a process for training temporary employees.

Solutions:	*(attach additional sheet if needed)*

Corrective Actions:	Assigned To	Due Date
1. Develop a training process for temporary material handlers.	L. Bell	7/10/2008
2. Train temporary material handlers and retrain existing material handlers in SOP #MH004.	J. Jones	7/10/2008
3. Create a training checklist for temporary material handlers.	K. Smith	7/15/2008

Preventive Actions:	Assigned To	Due Date
1. Determine which activities temporary employees can be assigned to throughout the company.	M. Collins	7/15/2008
2. Establish a companywide process for training temporary employees.	S. Robinson	7/25/2008

Verification:
Reviewed flowchart that described training process for temporary material handlers.
Reviewed training records of material handlers for SOP #MH004.
Reviewed training checklist for temporary material handlers (Form MH0017).
Looked at list of approved activities for temporary employees.
Reviewed the flowchart that described the companywide training process for temporary employees.
Verified training effectiveness of material handlers by observing them performing their job against procedures.
Verified training effectiveness of other temporary employees by observing their performance against procedures.

Signature	*Betty Simpson*	Date:	9/25/2008

Date Closed: __9/25/2008__   Reissue: No __X__   New PRR# _____
                                        Yes _____

Appendix A
Corrective Action Process

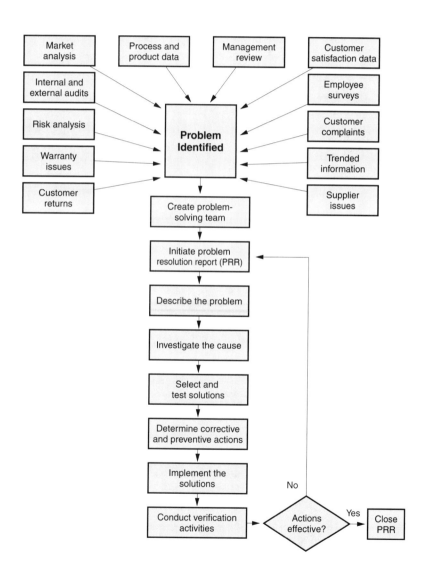

Market analysis

Process and product data

Management review

Customer satisfaction data

Internal and external audits

Employee surveys

Risk analysis

Problem Identified

Customer complaints

Warranty issues

Trended information

Customer returns

Supplier issues

Create problem-solving team

Initiate problem resolution report (PRR)

Describe the problem

Investigate the cause

Select and test solutions

Determine corrective and preventive actions

Implement the solutions

Conduct verification activities

No

Actions effective?

Yes

Close PRR

Appendix B
Preventive Action Process

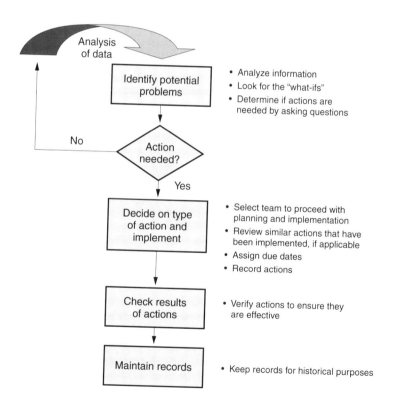

Analysis
of data

Identify potential
problems

- Analyze information
- Look for the "what-ifs"
- Determine if actions are
  needed by asking questions

No

Action
needed?

Yes

Decide on type
of action and
implement

- Select team to proceed with
  planning and implementation
- Review similar actions that have
  been implemented, if applicable
- Assign due dates
- Record actions

Check results
of actions

- Verify actions to ensure they
  are effective

Maintain records

- Keep records for historical purposes

Appendix C
Problem Solving at a Glance

Step	Action	Purpose
1. Describe the problem	• Use the 4W/2H/1C formula • Describe in clear terms • Do not jump to conclusions or solutions	• Clarifies problem for those who need to act
2. Investigate the cause	• Develop an investigation plan • Use problem-solving tools • Identify the root cause	• To ensure that the root of the problem is discovered and future problems prevented
3. Select and test solutions	• Brainstorm potential solutions • Conduct impact analysis • Determine the best solution(s) • Test	• To gain consensus on a prevention-based solution and conduct tests if needed
4. Implement the solutions	• Determine corrective and preventive action • Assign ownership and due dates • Monitor the actions for completion	• To ensure action is taken as planned
5. Verify and monitor the solutions	• Determine verification and monitoring activities • Conduct verification activities • Determine effectiveness of implemented actions	• To follow up on the actions to ensure they work

Appendix D
Problem Resolution Report

Problem Resolution Report

Initiation Date: _____   PRR# _____

Initiated By: _____

Problem Description:

Interim Actions: (Fast Fix)	Assigned To	Due Date

Root Cause:

Solutions: *(attach additional sheet if needed)*

Corrective Actions:	Assigned To	Due Date

Preventive Actions:	Assigned To	Due Date

Verification:

Signature		Date:	

Date Closed: _____   Reissue: No _____   New PRR# _____
                                       Yes _____

Appendix E
Investigation Action Plan Checklist

Investigation Action Plan Checklist	
Describe the fast fix that was taken (if applicable):	
Is the fix working at the moment? (If not, explain what will be done in the short term.)	Yes
	No
List the owner of the problem: List those who need to be involved:	
List information currently available to assist in the investigation: Data: Employee input: Flowcharts of the process: Procedures: Records including SPC charts, measurements, and other quantitative data:	
Has the problem occurred in the past? Yes/No If yes, what records exist?	
Frequency of meetings: (daily, weekly, etc.) Time: Place: First meeting date:	

Appendix F
Impact Analysis

Impact Analysis			
Root Cause:			
Proposed Solution(s):			
Analysis	**How will the solution impact the system?**	**Positive** ✓	**Negative** ✓
Cost			
Safety			
Product			
Process/System			
Customer			
Supplier			

Key:

1. *Cost:* What will the solution cost? (Include materials, wages, equipment, etc.)
2. *Safety Issues:* Will anyone be put in jeopardy because of this solution?
3. *Product Issues:* Will the product still meet spec?
4. *Process/System Issues:* Will other processes or systems be negatively affected? Will there be a compliance issue if the solution is implemented?
5. *Customer:* Will they still get what they want?
6. *Supplier:* Can the supplier remain the same?

Appendix G
Continual Improvement Process

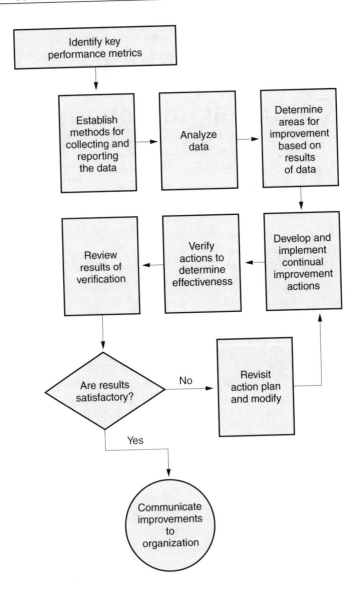

Endnotes

INTRODUCTION

1. ANSI/ISO/ASQ Q9001:2008 is the American-adopted standard identical to ISO 9001:2008.

CHAPTER 1

1. Philip Crosby, *Quality Is Free* (New York: McGraw-Hill, 1984; Plume, 1985): 66–73.
2. Joseph Juran, *Juran on Leadership for Quality* (New York: The Free Press, 1989): 21.
3. Howard S. Gitlow and Shelly J. Gitlow, *The Deming Guide to Quality and Competitive Position* (Englewood Cliffs, NJ: Prentice Hall, 1987): 69–96.
4. *ANSI/ISO/ASQ Q9000:2005 Quality Management Systems—Fundamentals and Vocabulary* (Milwaukee: ASQ Quality Press, 2006).

CHAPTER 2

1. Bjørn Andersen and Tom Fagerhaug, *Root Cause Analysis* (Milwaukee: ASQ Quality Press, 2000): 84.

CHAPTER 8

1. Joseph M. Juran, *Juran on Leadership for Quality: An Executive Handbook* (New York: The Free Press, 1989): 171.

CHAPTER 9

1. Bruce W. Tuckman, "Development Sequence in Small Groups," *Psychological Bulletin* 63 (1965): 384–99.
2. Bruce W. Tuckman and Mary Ann Jensen, *Refining and Developing Model* (1977).

CHAPTER 10

1. Joseph M. Juran, *Juran on Leadership for Quality: An Executive Handbook* (New York: The Free Press, 1989): 40.
2. Philip B. Crosby, *Quality without Tears* (New York: McGraw-Hill, 1984): 85–86.

References

ANSI/ISO/ASQ Q9000:2005 Quality Management Systems—Fundamentals and Vocabulary . Milwaukee: ASQ Quality Press, 2006.

ANSI/ISO/ASQ Q9004:2000 Quality Management Systems—Guidelines for Performance Improvements. Milwaukee: ASQ Quality Press, 2001.

Capezio, Peter, and Debra Morehouse. *Taking the Mystery out of TQM.* Hawthorne, NJ: Career Press, 1993.

Crosby, Philip B. *Quality Is Free.* New York: McGraw-Hill, 1979.

———. *Quality without Tears.* New York: McGraw-Hill, 1984.

Edwards, Paul, Sarah Edwards, and Rick Benzel. *Teaming Up.* New York: Jeremy P. Tarcher/Putnam, 1997.

Gitlow, Howard S., and Shelly J. Gitlow. *The Deming Guide to Quality and Competitive Position.* Englewood Cliffs, NJ: Prentice Hall, 1987.

Juran, Joseph M. *Juran on Leadership for Quality: An Executive Handbook.* New York: The Free Press, 1989.

Ketola, Jeanne, and Kathy Roberts. *ISO 9001:2000 Management Responsibility in a Nutshell.* Chico, CA: Paton Press, 2001.

Pokras, Sandy. *Systematic Problem-Solving and Decision-Making.* Los Altos, CA: Crisp Publications, 1989.

Tague, Nancy R. *The Quality Toolbox.* Milwaukee: ASQC Quality Press, 1995.

Total Quality Tools. Miamisburg, OH: QIP and PQ Systems, 1995.

Weaver, Charles N. *Managing the Four Stages of TQM.* Milwaukee: ASQC Quality Press, 1995.

About the Authors

Jeanne Ketola is the owner of Pathway Consulting, LLC. She has more than 20 years of business experience in a wide range of industries as a manager, consultant, trainer, and third party auditor. She specializes in developing quality management systems from scratch, resulting in successful ISO registrations. Ketola is a former five-time Minnesota Quality Award Examiner, ASQ Certified Quality Auditor, and certified, RAB Quality Management Systems Auditor. She is a trained management coach and an active member of the U.S. Technical Advisory Group to Technical Committee 176 that writes the standard. She is also the former secretary of the ANSI Z1 Executive Committee, which is responsible for all actions relating to national quality standards. Ketola has written many articles on the topic of ISO 9001 which appeared in *Quality Digest, Quality Progress, Springs,* and *The Informed Outlook.* She is also a national speaker on the topic and is the author of three international best sellers, *ISO 9000:2000 In a Nutshell, ISO 9001:2000 Management Responsibility In a Nutshell* and *Correct, Prevent, Improve!* She co-authored "The BEST Audit Checklist," a CD Rom to assist auditors in audit preparation. Her third book, *Correct, Prevent, Improve!* is also available in Spanish through the American Society for Quality.

Kathy Roberts is the CEO of The BlueWater Group, Inc. a management consulting firm specializing in business system analysis, development, and implementation. She holds a BS in Industrial Engineering and has 19 years of experience in industries including automotive, medical, clinical research, aerospace, electronics, textiles, chemicals and industrial paper. Kathy is a past member of the U.S. Technical Advisory Group that is responsible for developing and approving international management system standards for the United States. Kathy is a past section chair and a past regional councilor for the American Society for Quality, a past examiner for the North Carolina Performance Excellence Process, and a past certified quality auditor (CQA). Kathy has written many articles on the topic of ISO 9000 which have appeared in *Quality Digest* and *Quality Progress* and has been an international speaker. She is the co-author of three international best sellers on ISO 9001, *ISO 9000:2000 in a Nutshell, ISO 9001:2000 Management Responsibility in a Nutshell,* and *The BEST Audit Checklist ISO 9001:2000.* Her third book, *Correct, Prevent, Improve!* is also available in Spanish through the American Society for Quality.

Index